ARDUINO PROGRAMMING

The Ultimate Intermediate Guide to Learn
Arduino Programming Step by Step

Table of Contents

INTRODUCTION

Congratulations on taking the next step and purchasing *Arduino Programming: The Ultimate Intermediate Guide to Learn Arduino Programming Step By Step*. The goal of this book is to extend the knowledge you already built up using the previous book in the series.

Progressing from the beginner level to intermediary is no easy task, as many students give up due to the pressure involved in working with hardware, coding patterns, and various tools. You took this step, and this book will reward you for it by guiding you to the next level. You will learn how to build interesting projects using the Arduino board, and you will also be working with real world application examples.

The main purpose of *Arduino Programming: The Ultimate Intermediate Guide to Learn Arduino Programming Step By Step* is to give you all the tools you need to build more powerful projects and applications. You will learn how to improve your programming and how to improve your Arduino projects by boosting its power and using various modules. You will learn how to apply and code those modules to create advanced storage systems, networks, and even an Arduino global positioning system.

This book will guide you step by step through all the techniques, concepts, and tools you need. There will also be real world examples through which you will learn how to make the right connections, and how to implement your code. Project-based work is the best kind of work when it comes to learning more advanced topics.

How to Benefit the Most

As already mentioned, this book isn't just about theory. In every chapter and every section, you will encounter real world projects and study them step by step. You will learn how to connect physical modules to the Arduino, and how to write the firmware so that they function properly. This means that in order to benefit from this book, you have to practice alongside with it. Do not skip over practical examples, as they are crucial to understand the implementation of various techniques in other projects.

The practical examples contained in this book are real world projects that rely on widely available electronics and software components. Don't worry about the budget, because all of the modules you will work with are cheap and readily available in any electronics store. The programming part of the projects is also easy to understand, and even if you encounter difficulties, it is easy to research outside of this guide. All of the code, libraries, and applications can be found in a large number of places, as they are open source and used to teach students all over the world. If you get stuck, don't be afraid to join an online community of Arduino enthusiasts. You can learn a lot more with help from those who have the same interests as you. Plus, it's much more fun to work on a project when you can talk about it to others who understand you.

With that being said, you'll get the most benefit out of this book by putting everything you learn into practice. The key here is practice, practice, practice!

CHAPTER 1: PROGRAMMING IMPROVEMENTS

No matter the project, you need to prepare your work environment and think about the elements that will make your code logical, readable, and simply beautiful to look at. In this chapter we are going to discuss improving your programming with functions, math, and calculation optimization.

In the previous book, *Arduino Programming: The Ultimate Beginner's Guide to Learn Arduino Programming Step by Step*, we discussed the basics of programming as well as Arduino functions, however we didn't go into too much detail. In this chapter we will explore them further, and build on your knowledge of mathematics and trigonometry as well.

Functions

In this section we are going to go over the basics to refresh your memory, because we need to later dive into more detail. The foundation is extremely important, especially because we need to go over mathematical and trigonometric functions soon.

As you should already know, a function simply refers to code that can be used and reused from any section of the program. In a program written in C, a function has a unique name, it is global and can require arguments, as well as return results.

With the Arduino IDE a function prototype can be created automatically, however sometimes we have to declare it ourselves. This can be done in one single code file in the beginning. For instance, let's say we want a function that returns the sum of two integers as a result. We will have two variables that are integers, and therefore our result will also be an integer. Here's the example in code:

int mySum (int x, int y);

Now that we have our basic prototype, we can see that it is identical to the header. The function's header is simply the first statement definition. Here's how the structure of the function looks:

```
int mySum (int x, int y) // the header

{

    // the body

}
```

The general structure of the header is simply returnType functionName (arguments). The returnType is a variable, and when the function doesn't return any result we need to state it as equal to void. The functionName can be any name you choose, just make sure to always use an easy to understand name that describes what the function is all about. Keep in mind that code readability is crucial to a clean and improved code, so you don't want to have functions such as mathFunction1. In case you weren't aware, Arduino, as well as C, respects the Camelcase naming convention, so label your functions like "mySum" for instance. As for the arguments, they are just variable declarations that are in fact optional. You don't always have to declare the arguments, especially when you want a function to result in an action that is always the same.

The function's body is where we find all the detailed instructions. You can simply refer to it as "the code" because this is where everything happens. Variables are defined, conditions are laid, and loops come out to play. Now let's take the mySum function and give it a body:

```
int mySum (int x, int y) // the header

{

    int result; // the variable that contains our result

    result = x + y; // the operation is performed and then stored in the result

    return result;  // returns the result

}
```

Now let's take a look at an Arduino code example of the same process:

```
void setup() {

Serial.begin (9600) ; An awesome example of Arduino code

}

Void loop() {

    int currentResult;

for (int i = 0 ; in < 100 ; i++)

{

    currentResult = mySum (i, i + 1);

    Serial.println (currentResult)

}

Delay (2000) ; perform a pause for 2 seconds

}

    int mySum (int x, int y)

{

    int result;

    result = x + y;

    return result;

}
```

The code should be self-explanatory, but the most important aspect of this example is that we make the call first and the function follows with the return of the result from the calculation. In other words, a function's "call" statement that returns a result is a value.

Now that we quickly recapped the basics of functions, let's discuss what the benefits are and why we should always use them.

The Benefits of Functions

As already mentioned, code needs to be readable and well-structured. If you are still a beginner programmer, you might be tempted to stick to the basics and avoid functions. This is a grave mistake, and you should use functions as much as possible in order to split your code into optimal segments. With that being said, here are the advantages of using functions and how they can improve your programming skills:

1. **Easier coding and readability**: Stay organized with clean code. When you first write your code, you will often use a lot of common statements that repeat themselves. The general rule accepted by most programmers is that if you write something more than twice, it's time to turn it into a function. You should never repeat yourself. You will also have a much easier time debugging your code. Instead of checking individual statements, you can simply debug the function and everything with-

in it with be fixed.

2. **Reusability**: You will always have sections of code that are for general use and frequently needed, and higher level code that is rarely needed. For instance, you might create a function that converts Euros to US Dollars. This is a general purpose function that you might call very often. However, you might also create a function that converts USD into Norwegian Crowns, but it is rarely needed. The point is that in both cases you are reusing code, meaning that whenever the case arises you have a prepared function that simply needs to be called. Reusable code cuts down on your programming time so that you can focus on other tasks.

Mathematical Functions and Arduino

Mathematical functions are part of the C standard library and will work with Arduino as well. Many of these functions are also inherited in C++, however there are some differences when it comes to complex numbers. In C++ complex number handling isn't provided by the C library, but instead from its own which uses the following class template:

std: : complex

Take note, all of the mathematical functions will work well with floating point numbers. In C, the library is math.h and it needs to be called inside a program's header. Once it's mentioned, we can call any mathematical functions we need, such as the trigonometric functions.

Trigonometric Functions

In many cases, we have to perform trigonometric calculations in order to determine a distance which an object travelled, angular speed, and so on. Often, these operations need to take place inside the Arduino core, especially when you need to use it as an autonomous unit without a computer around. The basic trigonometric functions are provided inside the core, so let's discuss them briefly. A large part of the functions will return a radian as a result, because it is a unit that is used by most of them. Therefore, you should have some knowledge about radians, degrees, how to perform a conversion operation, and trigonometry in general.

A radian is the unit of measure for angles, and it is often used instead of degrees. For instance, a circle that measures in 360 degrees measures in slightly more than 6 radians. A degree is 1/360 of a circle, and since a circle can be measured as 2π, we can perform the conversion easily like so:

angle radian = angle degree * $\pi/180$

angle degree = angle radian * $180/\pi$

Now let's define the sine, cosine, and tangent, with x being the angle measured in radians:

Sin(x) = opposite / hypotenuse

Cos(x) = adjacent / hypotenuse

Tan(x) = sin(x) / cos(x) = opposite / adjacent

Keep in mind that the sine and cosine go from a value of angles measured in radians of -1 to 1. The tangent, on the other hand, has certain points where it lacks a definition and therefore it evolves cyclically from negative infinity to positive infinity. The functions infinitely oscillate and we can use them for pure operations. Now that we can determine the sine, cosine, and tangent when there's an angle, let's establish how to determine the angle when we have the sine, cosine, and tangent.

In the scenario just mentioned, we need to use inverse trigonometric functions, namely the arcsine, arccosine, and arctangent. Here we have the inverse process of the previous functions, however they can supply us with many angles. Let's say we have a y integer and write the following mathematical connections:

sin (A) = x ó A = arcsin(x) + 2kπ or y = π − arcsin(x) + 2kπ

cos (A) = x ó A = arccos(x) + 2kπ or y = 2π − arccos (x) + 2kπ

tan (A) = x ó A = arctan(x) + kπ

Next, let's see the trigonometric function's prototype that can be found inside the Arduino core as well as the math.h library:

double sin (double x); returns the sine of x radians

double cos (double x); returns the cosine of x radians

double tan (double x); returns the tangent of x radians

double asin (double x); returns A, the angle corresponding to sin (A) = x

double acos (double x); returns A, the angle corresponding to cos (A) = x

double atan (double x); returns A, the angle corresponding to tan (A) = x

double atan2 (double y, double x); returns arctan (y/x)

When we need to perform mathematical calculations, we don't always rely on the trigonometric functions. Even for a simple operation, we can use exponential functions (and others), which are provided by Arduino as well. Here are some of the most common ones that you will use:

double pow (double x, double y); returns x to power y

double exp (double x); returns the exponential value of x

double log (double x); returns the natural logarithm of x with x > 0

double log10 (double x); returns the logarithm of x to base 10 with x > 0

double square (double x); returns the square of x

double sqrt (double x); returns the square root of x with x >= 0

double fabs (double x); returns the absolute value of x

So why would we use these operations? Let's say you are working on a basic Arduino project and you need to use a sensor to measure the temperature. You might be tempted to simply work with the inputs and outputs and not even make any conversions because it's not truly necessary. However, you can use these functions to achieve your goal and even optimize the firmware. With that being said, let's discuss calculation optimization.

Calculation Optimizations

In this section we aren't going to discuss all of the advanced programming optimization techniques, but we will explore methods of optimizing on pure calculations.

As you already know, the process of developing a project involves three steps: design, coding, and optimization. However, these development stages aren't as valid when it comes to small programs. Simpler projects are optimized directly in the coding process. This means that with each line of code you write, you should be thinking how you can optimize it. With that being said, do not sacrifice code readability just so you can fulfill various optimization processes.

Bit Shift Operations

Let's take an array as a simple example for calculation optimization. You might be inclined to use a multiplication operation when you perform the array indexing. However, doing so is extremely hard on your CPU resources, so you should seek to optimize. The easiest solution is to simply opt for working with an array declared with a power of two size, such as 512 instead of 500. Let's explore the "why."

People are taught to think in the decimal numeral system, meaning you count as follows: 0, 1, 2, 3, 4, 5, 6, 7, 8, 9, 10, etc. Computers, on the other hand, think in a binary numeral system instead, and they count as follows: 0, 1, 10, 11, 100, 101, 110, 111, etc. With that in mind, let's discuss the four bitwise operators:

Bitwise AND: We write this operator with an ampersand, "&" and it operates on every single bit position by following these rules:

0 & 0 == 0

0 & 1 == 0

1 & 0 == 0

1 & 1 == 1

Now let's see an example using integers:

int x = 35; // 00000000 00100011 in binary

int y = 49; // 00000000 00110001 in binary

int z = x & y; // 00000000 00100001 in binary, and 33 in decimal

Keep in mind that an integer has a 16-bit value. In our example we are comparing each bit, one at a time, for every position, based on the operator's rules.

Bitwise OR: This operator is represented by a vertical line "|". Here are the rules by which it operates on every single bit position:

0 | 0 == 0

0| 1 == 1

1| 0 == 1

1 | 1 == 1

Bitwise XOR: This operator is represented by a single caret "^" and it operates on every single bit position like so:

0 ^ 0 == 0

0 ^ 1 == 1

1 ^ 0 == 1

1 ^ 1 == 0

Bitwise NOT: This operator is represented by the tilde symbol "~". It can only be applied to a single number, meaning that it is a unary operator. Basically, it swaps every bit to its own opposite, like so:

~ 0 == 1

~ 1 == 0

Here's how an example with integers looks:

int x = 35; // 00000000 00100011 in binary

int y = ~x; // 11111111 11011100 (opposite of x), and -36 in decimal

Now that you know about bitwise operators, let's continue with the bit shift operation, which is the main attraction in this section.

The left shift operator is represented by "<<" and the right shift operator is represented by ">>". Now let's see how it is applied in a real example:

int x = 36; // 00000000 00100100

int y = x << 2; // 00000000 10010000, 144

int z = x >> 1; // 00000000 00010010, 18

As you may have worked out on your own, we have shifted the bits from a number of positions to the left, or to the right. You may have also noticed that performing << 1 is the same as multiplying by two, and >> is the same as dividing by two.

Bitwise operations are all about performance. They are primitive and supported directly by the computer's processors, especially when it comes to embedded systems. Using bitwise operations can significantly boost your performance and cause a much smaller resource drain. You should use the power of two as the array size because it will push the use of bit shift operators internally while the processor will perform the index calculations. Since multiplications and divisions can be easily done using a bit shift, you should eventually replace all of them that are by the power of two with bit shifting. Working with this type of operation will still keep your code clean and readable enough while also optimizing it.

Lookup Tables

Pay attention to the use of lookup tables, as they are one of the best tools at your disposal while programming. A lookup table is an array that consists of predetermined values. This means that resource heavy runtime calculations are replaced with an array index operation that is much simpler and easier to process. Imagine the following scenario. Your job is to track an object's location by using sensors to determine the distance. This means you will rely mostly on trigonometric calculations and perhaps power calculations as well. They are heavy resource consumers, therefore your processor will have to allocate a lot of power to perform these functions. Luckily, the easiest solution is to use array content reading instead of performing those mathematical calculations.

Lookup tables are simply stored inside a static program's memory once they are pre-calculated. You can also calculate them during a program's initialization stage. This method is a variation that is known as a pre-fetched lookup table.

The key is to pay attention to the functions that are draining the CPU's power. Trigonometric calculations are perfect examples of resource intensive computations, especially when working with embedded systems that have far more limited resources than a computer.

With the theory in mind, let's now take a look at how we can initialize lookup tables and take advantage of their power.

Application

The first step we need to take in the table initialization process is pre-calculating the cosine lookup table. The goal here is to build a precision system where we can call cos(x) and gain all of x's values. However, keep in mind that the values inside an array are of a limited size, and therefore if we want to pre-fetch them we need to calculate the finite number of values. This means that we will not be able to have cos(x) results for the total number of float values, but only for the ones that were calculated.

Let's work on an Arduino code example where we take the

precision as a 0.5 degree angle:

```
float cosLookup [(int) ( 360.0  * 1 / 0.5)] ;

const float DEG2RAD = 180 / PI ;

const fl0at cosPrecision = 0.5;

cons tint cosPeriod = (int) (360.0 * 1 / cosPrecision) ;

void setup ()

{

    initCosLUT();

}

void loop()

{

    //empty for the moment

}

void initCosLUT

    for (int i = 0 ; i < cosPeriod ; i++)

    {

    cosLookup[i] = (float) cos (i * DEG2RAD * cosPreci-
    sion) ;
```

```
    }

}
```

We declared cosLookup as a float array that has a specific size. We are using 260 * 1 / precision as the number of components that are needed inside the array. In our example we have a precision of 0.5 degrees, which we can make even simpler with the following line:

```
float cosLookup [720]
```

We also added a constant in order to be able to convert the degrees into radians (DEG2RAD), and then we introduced the cosPrecision and cosPeriod so that the calculations are executed only once. Next up, we have the initCosLUT function that is used to make the pre-calculation within the setup function. Inside of it there's a loop that pre-calculates the value of cosine(x) for every x value that is between 0 and 2π. During the initialization process, the lookup table values are determined and further calculation is provided by an array index operation.

Our next step is to replace any pure calculation with array index operations. Let's retrieve the cosine values by accessing the lookup table using the following function:

```
float myFastCos (float angle) {

 return cosLookup [(int) ( angle * 1 / cosPrecision) % cosPeriod] ; }
```

We establish the angle by taking the precision of the lookup table into consideration. A modulo operation is used with the cosPeriod value in order to cover the values of any higher angles to the limit of the lookup table. This is how we have the index and therefore return the array value based on it.

Time

Since we're working with embedded software, being able to play with time is always interesting. In this section we are going to discuss the time functions provided by the Arduino core library and how we can perform some optimization operations. There's even an extremely precise function that is capable of achieving an 8 microsecond resolution.

Arduino's board chip provides us with "uptime" which represents the time from the moment the board was started. What does that mean? The board needs to stay powered up if we want to store a time and date.

Now let's discuss the main function, which is "millis." What does it do? It simply returns how many milliseconds have passed since the board was turned on. Keep in mind that according to the documentation, the number will be reset once 50 days pass. This is referred to as time overflow. Now let's create a program which measures and prints the uptime to the serial monitor once every 250 milliseconds.

```
unsigned long measuredTime;

void setup(){
```

```
    Serial.begin(9600);

}

void loop(){

    Serial.print("Time: ");

    measuredTime = millis();

    Serial.println(measuredTime);

    delay(250);

}
```

The code is quite self-explanatory, even for a beginner. As a side note, this is a great demonstration why code readability matters and every programmer should focus time to practice it. With that being said, let's now ask ourselves how we can optimize this program. Naturally, this is a tiny program that doesn't truly need optimization, however we can avoid using the variable "measuredTime" and simplify it ever so slightly. Here's what the optimized version would look like:

```
void setup(){

    Serial.begin(9600);

}
```

```
void loop(){

    Serial.print("Time: ");

    Serial.println(millis());

    delay(250);

}
```

Every bit of simplicity makes your program more readable, easier to debug, and less vulnerable to errors and unnecessary resource drains. Simplicity is beautiful, don't forget that.

Next up, we can optimize our program in a different way by increasing its precision with the "micros" function. The uptime can have a precision of 8 microseconds, however the time overflow will be around 70 minutes instead of 50 days. In other words, we need to sacrifice time overflow in exchange for precision. Here's how it's done in code:

```
void setup(){

    Serial.begin(9600);

}

void loop(){

    Serial.print(«Time in ms: «);

    Serial.println(millis());

    Serial.print(«Time in µs: «);
```

```
        Serial.println(micros());

        delay(250);

    }
```

Now that you know more about code optimization, even for the smallest Arduino projects, we can start exploring practical applications where objects can communicate with each other and react to you based on your actions.

CHAPTER 2: DIGITAL INPUTS

As you may already know the Arduino boards have a number of inputs and outputs, which provide headers that directly connect to the ATMega chipset legs. An input or an output can be wired directly to any component without requiring soldering techniques, thus making the Arduino a lot easier to work with and less messy.

Just in case you need a reminder, the Arduino has both analog and digital inputs, while the digital outputs can be forced to imitate the analog ones. In this chapter we are going to focus on digital inputs and the ability to sense the outside world. We will also discuss "Processing," which is an open source IDE and graphical library that allows you to visualize your operations graphically. Finally, we are going to experiment with switches and design a communication protocol between software and hardware.

Perceiving the Outside World

While we are currently living in a highly digitized world, not everything relies on sensors in order to perform various actions or reactions. However, humans rely on biological sensors like skin that detect temperature changes, eyes that react to light, ears that detect air movements, and a nose and mouth that process chemical compounds. Basically, we have the ability to record data and provide it for perception. In a similar manner, the Arduino board can also sense the world by having the capacity to provide some data in order to perceive the world.

Sensors are physical convertors that measure and quantify a physical state that is then translated into a signal that can be processed and understood by computers, as well as people. For instance, we used a thermometer that relies on a substance that contracts or dilates in order to give us readable data on the present temperature. The Arduino can sense in the same manner using a connected sensor. In the beginner's guide for the Arduino, we briefly discussed working with analog sensors using an analog to digital converter.

Here we are going to focus on digital sensors that can quantify any environmental conditions such as temperature, pressure, humidity, electromagnetism, light, wind speed, motion, and so on. The list is nearly endless, as there are a variety of digital sensors you can work with and all of them provide some kind of data from a measurement. While humans detect and quantify temperature by sensing it through the skin, digital sensors rely on a conversion system similar to thermometers. Thermometers rely on a volume that depends on the temperature. The height that the liquid inside it reaches is converted to a certain number of Celsius, Fahrenheit, or Kelvin degrees. This is what is known as a double conversion, and the sensors operate just like the thermometer, by integrating mathematical calculations to provide us with the data we need. However, the data that is provided by the sensor needs to be read by our Arduino board. If we use a digital thermal sensor, we first need to power it up, but we also need to measure the power potential that is generated from the pins, otherwise we wouldn't be able to perceive the temperature value. In other words, the Arduino needs to convert this power potential into something we can read and understand. This is a basic conversion that needs to be translated and explained so that we can perceive it. But what about computers?

Computers rule over the digital domain, which is exactly the opposite of the analog domain. Everything that is analog is related to a physical measure, and the Arduino provides us with an analog input, but no output. To further understand the concept you should think about the input as a collection of reading pins, and the output as a collection of writing pins. The Arduino essentially reads what the world offers and then writes back to the world. A digital pin is set to provide us with the ability to read the power potential and convert to 0 or 1 (we will elaborate on this with switches). Now let's illustrate the theory with the help of Processing.

Processing

As mentioned earlier, Processing is an IDE and a programming language (sort of) that you can use for graphical representations. It is essentially a framework that is used to perform programming tasks through visual feedback, instead of actual programming that can be extremely abstract. Processing is the blank sheet of paper on which you can write or draw without relying on too much programming knowledge. However, we can't truly call it a programming language on its own, as it relies on a subset of Java and a number of external libraries.

Processing relies on the Java language but offers visual programming and a simplified syntax. The compilation process is also simplified, as it works just like the Arduino IDE. Now let's set it up by first downloading from processing.org/download/. Keep in mind that this framework doesn't need to be installed in the typical sense. All you need to do is place it on your computer, depending on your operating system, and simply run it. Once you start it up, you will be greeted by the Processing IDE which may seem very similar to the Arduino one. As a fun fact, you should know that you can call Processing Arduino's father, since the Arduino IDE has been taken from Processing.

Now, if you go to Files > Examples Basics you can find demonstrations for array objects and everything you need. Processing offers you everything you need to easily code, compile, and run. Now let's try out the following code and see why Processing is fun to use whether you are at a beginner, intermediate, or advanced level.

```
int particlesNumber = 80;

float[] positionsX = new float[particlesNumber]; // storing
the particles
```

```
X-coordinates    float[]    positionsY   =    new
float[particlesNumber]; // particles Y-coordinates

float[] radii = new float[particlesNumber];

float[] easings = new float[particlesNumber];

void setup() {

    size(600, 600); // the size of the environment

    noStroke(); // the shape we draw will have no stroke

    // loop initializing easings & radii for all particles

    for (int i=0 ; i < particlesNumber ; i++)

    {

        easings[i] = 0.04 * i / particlesNumber;

        radii[i] = 30 * i / particlesNumber;

    }

}

// draw is run infinitely

void draw() {

    background(34); // our environment's background color

    float targetX = mouseX;
```

```
float targetY = mouseY;

for (int i=0 ; i < particlesNumber ; i++)

{

    float dx = targetX - positionsX[i];

    if (abs(dx) > 1) { // if distance > 1, update position
    positionsX[i] += dx * easings[i];

}

float dy = targetY - positionsY[i];

if (abs(dy) > 1) {

positionsY[i] += dy * easings[i];

}

// changing the color

fill(255 * i / particlesNumber);

// drawing the i particle

ellipse(positionsX[i], positionsY[i], radii[i], radii[i]);

}

}
```

Now run this block of Java code and move your mouse around the environment. Processing will show you a fun graphical visualization of a series of particles that follow every movement of the mouse. Keep in mind that while so far you worked with C programming, you should be able to easily understand Java, as this language derives from C. Now let's talk more about the code.

We have three important code sections. In the first part we declare all the variables and definitions. Then we have the setup function that is only run on startup, and lastly we have the draw function that runs forever until you tell it to stop. As you can see, all of these functions play a similar role, both in Processing as well as Arduino. That's because we are using the same design pattern with both tools. We begin by initiating a variable to store the particles, and then we introduce a number of arrays for every single particle we create. This design pattern is commonly used with Processing because of how readable and functional it is.

Processing and Arduino go hand in hand as they both are well-developed with a massive community built around them, open source, and available for all computer operating systems. This means that anyone can use both technologies no matter their current skill level. Many choose to work with Processing because of how easy it is to use when it comes to data visualization. Illustrating complex information with the help of basic graphical shapes can provide more insight than raw, abstract data can.

In the next section, you will learn how to combine the functionality of Processing with Arduino by building a simple communication protocol.

Linking the Physical to the Virtual

In this section, we are going to use Arduino for what it was meant to do, and link the physical to the virtual by creating a communication protocol between hardware and software. Before we begin work on our project, you should refresh your knowledge on switches.

Switches are simple hardware components that interrupt an electrical circuit. While there are several types of switches, we are only interested in two of them. One is the toggle, and the second is called a momentary, or push for action. The switches you are most familiar with are the toggles, because nearly everything you use involves one of them. The toggle works by pushing it when you want a certain action to be performed, and then release it without breaking that action. The momentary, on the other hand, needs to be continuously pushed in order for the action to occur.

Now for our project, you will have to take your knowledge from the previous book, and apply it in order to build a circuit. You will need a breadboard, wires, and we are going to use a momentary switch. First we're going to connect the ground and the +5 V of the Arduino to the top rails of the breadboard, and then use a few other rails to wire the board. There's no need to get entangled in unnecessarily long wires. Next, we will use a resistor between pin 2 and ground. The momentary switch goes between pin 2 and the +5 V line. We are going to use pin 2 as an input.

Now that we have the simple part down, let's talk about that resistor. The digital pin that we prepared to be an input is capable of sinking current, which essentially means that it works as if it was connected to ground. Provided that we have adequate firmware, we can check the digital pin and make sure it provides us with a readable value. In our example, we should be able to translate an electrical potential of 5V as a high value, and a close to 0V electrical potential as a low value. What can happen in this scenario is input signal noise that can be falsely read as an action. Because of this risk, we need to use a resistor, namely a pull-down resistor. This high impedance resistor allows a current sink to pin 2, therefore reducing any risks when operating at a close to 0 value. Both high and low values will be far more accurately detected with this type of resistor, however keep in mind that the energy requirement will be increased.

Now that the hardware is prepared, the next step is all about code. So what are the coding steps? First, we need to define the pins, as well as a variable for the state of the switch. Next, we need to set the LED pin and the switch pin as outputs, and then set up an infinite loop which will read and store the state of the input. In other words, the LED turns on if the input state is set to high, else it's turned off. Now let's see all of this in real code:

```
const int switchPin = 2;
```

```
const int ledPin = 13;

int switchState = 0;

state

void setup() {

    pinMode(ledPin, OUTPUT);

    pinMode(switchPin, INPUT);

}

void loop(){

    switchState = digitalRead(switchPin);

    if (switchState == HIGH) {

        digitalWrite(ledPin, HIGH); //turn on LED

    }

    else {

        digitalWrite(ledPin, LOW); // turn off LED

    }

}
```

Now that we have that board ready with the right coding behind it, let's connect the two sections of our project with the
power of Processing. We are going to use this tool to graphical-

ly display our manipulation of the switch. This phase requires the implementation of a serial communication protocol between Processing and Arduino, and we are going to design it only with the Arduino core.

As you may already know, a communication protocol is simply a rule set that is designed to guide the exchange of information between two parties, whether it's between a human and a computer or several computers. Here are the basic guidelines we need to follow when creating any basic communication protocol, including this one:

1. The protocol needs to be open to expansion in case we want to add new types of information that can be communicated.

2. Data transit is crucial, therefore we want our protocol to be able to transfer a good amount of information in a short amount of time

3. The last guideline is valid for everything you develop and it should always be on your mind. The code for the protocol needs to be readable and easy to understand by any outsider who may decide to try out your project.

Now let's discuss the design. We are going to have a two byte message that contains the switch state and the switch number. This type of message is the basic data packet you encounter in the real world extremely often. Next, we need to decide what we want to achieve. Let's say we want a circle that changes color depending on the state of the switch. If it's a dark color the switch is released, and if it's green then it's pressed. In order to write this in code, we first need to define and instantiate a serial port, followed by defining the current color to be dark. Next we need an infinite loop which will verify the receival of the serial port and the data. If this data tells the program that the state of the switch is off, the color goes from green to dark, otherwise the color will be green.

Now before we write the code, we need to use one of Processing's many integrated libraries. For our design to work, we need the serial library. To import it, you need to go to the Sketch tab, followed by Import Library and select "serial." That's it! Let's write the code:

```
import processing.serial.*;

Serial theSerialPort;

int[] serialBytesArray = new int[2]; //store the current
message inside array

int switchState;

int switchID;

int bytesCount = 0;

boolean init = false;

int fillColor = 40;

void setup(){
```

```
//define the graphical environment

size(500,500);

background(70);

noStroke();

println(Serial.list());

String thePortName = Serial.list()[0];

theSerialPort = new Serial(this, thePortName, 9600);

}

void draw(){

    fill(fillColor);

    ellipse(width/2, height/2, 230, 230);

}

void serialEvent(Serial myPort) {

    int inByte = myPort.read();

    if (init == false) {

    if (inByte == 'Z') {

    myPort.clear();

    init = true;

    myPort.write('Z');
```

```
        }
    }
    else {
        serialBytesArray[bytesCount] = inByte;
        bytesCount++;
        if (bytesCount > 1 ) {
            switchID = serialBytesArray[0];
            switchState = serialBytesArray[1];
            switch
            println(switchID + "\t" + switchState);
                if (switchState == 0) fillColor = 40;
                else fillColor = 255;
                myPort.write('Z');
                bytesCount = 0;
            }
        }
    }
```

Now let's discuss the process behind the implementation. We first need to create a Processing Serial Library object and a two integer sized array where we store our two byte messages from the Arduino. Next, we have a switch state and a switch ID which need to be stored in such a way to correspond to the messages we receive. The switch ID is only necessary because our design has expandability as an option, and this way we can tell the difference between multiple switches if we ever add them. Then we define init to false in the starting phase, but it switches to true once a byte is received from the Arduino.

In the second section of the implementation we define the actual environment of our graphical representation. We choose the colors, the size, and so on. Next up, we retrieve information on how many serial ports we have access to. This information is simply for debug purposes. This is all done inside the setup function which runs only once.

The third section is all about the draw function, which is quite simple. We have a fill color variable that is attached to a fill function where we instruct the program how to choose the different color and draw the circle. The circle is drawn using the ellipse function where we need to specify the x and y coordinates of the center, as well as the width and height. You may have noticed that the width and height have been chosen to be the same as the dimensions of the environment itself. This is because at some point you might want to resize the environment, and this way the circle is resized along with it with no further modifications to the code.

Finally, we have the serialEvent callback method. We use it in order to be more efficient instead of being forced to count every single time a serial port checks whether there's some data to read. We use myPort.read() to read the bytes we receive and perform the verification with the init variable. We need to see if the communication has already been established by checking whether we are dealing with the first message. If init tests as false and if the message that we receive from the Arduino is Z, then our program will clear a serial port and store information on the beginning of the communication. When this happens, the Z message is sent back to the Arduino as a response.

If communications have started, the bytes are stored into the serial bytes array and increment bytesCount. As long as we keep receiving bytes, and the count is smaller or equal to one, we concluded that the message is not whole, since it needs to be two bytes in size. Once we have the byte count equal to two, we have a whole message which we can divide into two variables, namely the switch ID and the switch state.

You can apply this approach to connecting multiple switches to the Arduino. In principle, nothing really changes and you already have the knowledge to achieve this step. With that being said, there is one more aspect regarding switches that needs to be clarified.

The Debounce Concept

In order to understand this concept, we need to peek at a microscopic level inside the switch. What is a switch and how is it made? Simply put, a switch is made out of bits and pieces of plastic and metal where we have a cap that is pressed to move a piece of metal which in turn connects to another piece of metal and thus closes the circuit. At this point, if we accurately measure the electric potential of the Arduino's digital pin, we will notice some noise that occurs approximately 1 ms after pressing the switch. This noise may seem insignificant, however it can lead to a lot of problems in any program that involves a switch.

So what happens when you press the button? There's a large chance that the counts will not be precise. For instance, if you press it once, the program might detect three or four actions. Or perhaps you pressed it four times, but only one press was registered. Any of these scenarios can occur and cause a lot of frustration. This is what we call bounce, and it has to do with the physical action of pressing the button. Keep in mind that typically when you press any button, the connection isn't fully achieved instantly. The signal may connect and break several times during the action, and this is what causes issues. It's not a defect or a design problem. It's simply how switches work.

Bouncing occurs within fractions of a second and you don't even notice it. However, the problem is that a microcontroller does notice it and detects it as more than one button press. This is why a program might detect one switch press as two or three. Bouncing leads to unwanted state changes. So how can this be fixed? Debouncing code is the answer.

There are two separate elements over which we have some control, and they are the circuit and the firmware. We can modify the circuit physically by adding capacitors, diodes, and various trigger inverters until we find the perfect balance, however this method is rather inconvenient and time consuming. This is why we are going to focus on resolving this issue through code. We are going to implement a filter based on time. Let's go through the code and see how it's done:

```
const int switchPin = 2;

const int ledPin = 13;

int switchState = 0;

int lastSwitchState= LOW;

long lastDebounceTime = 0;

long debounceDelay = 50;

void setup() {

    pinMode(ledPin, OUTPUT);

    pinMode(switchPin, INPUT);

}

void loop(){

    int readInput = digitalRead(switchPin);

        if (readInput != lastSwitchState){

        lastDebounceTime = millis();

        }
```

```
if ((millis() - lastDebounceTime) > debounceDelay
){

    switchState = readInput;

}

lastSwitchState = readInput;

if (switchState == HIGH)

{

    digitalWrite(ledPin, HIGH);

}

else

{

    digitalWrite(ledPin, LOW);

}

}
```

Our implementation of the debouncing concept can be broken down into several steps. We define a variable that is used to store the last read state, a variable that stores the time when the last debounce happened, and a delay variable. We use the millis function we discussed earlier as the time metric. Next, we have the loop cycle during which we read the input without storing it inside the switch state variable. We use this variable without changing it outside of the debounce process. Once we read the input during every cycle, we store it as a readInput variable, which we compare afterwards to the last switch state. If these variables are different, it means that some kind of change is happening, but it can either be a button press or simply a bounce. If it's an unwanted bounce, all we have to do is reset the counter. Lastly, we perform a check to compare the time since the last debounce and the delay. If it is concluded that it is larger than the delay, the cycle's last read input will be considered as the true switch state and it will be stored inside the proper variable. On the other hand, if the time since the last debounce is shorter than the delay, we will store the last read value inside the last switch state variable in order to perform a comparison check during the next cycle.

This implementation is a general one when it comes to software-based debouncing and it is used in many scenarios that involve switches and inputs corrupted by noise. In other words, anything that involves a human user can benefit from a debouncer. However, keep in mind that if we're working with system communications, debouncing won't accomplish anything. The only reason this concept is useful in the first scenario is because of the slow interactivity between user and system. Systems communicate between each other so fast that the period of time which is considered to be a real press is virtually non-existent.

CHAPTER 3: SERIAL COMMUNICATION

So far we can summarize the use of the Arduino to sharing and communicating signals. If we take it apart we can conclude that every component belonging to this device can in some way be prepared to react to a real world action and communicate data on it, whether to other components, computers, or humans.

In this chapter we are going to specifically focus on serial communication and the serial protocol. You might already know that this type of communication is used for computer to human interaction, however it is not limited only to that. Serial communication is also useful for devices to allow their own components to communicate with each other.

Are you still somewhat confused? What if you realized that serial communication is used in nearly every technology that you use on a daily basis? You may have heard of USB (of course you have), which stands for universal serial bus. This system represents a serial communication bus that is used by many higher level protocols. To lift the cloud even further, you should understand that serial communication is simply a way of sending information bit by bit through a communication bus. With that being said, let's discuss some general aspects of this concept.

General Aspects

When we discuss serial communication, we also have to include parallel communication, which is in fact its opposite.
What's the difference? Let's assume we need to send eight bits
of data from the speaker to the listener. If we are using serial
communication, the bits will be transmitted one after another
through the same channel. However, if we are using parallel
communication, the eight bits will be sent at the same time
through eight different channels. No matter the distance or the
circumstances, serial communication will manage to outper-
form the parallel form, even though you might think it's slow-
er. Sending all eight bits of data simultaneously isn't the best
solution for the following reasons:

1. Parallel communication requires the same number of
    connections, or wires, as the number of bits of data that
    need to be sent to the listener. This can result in re-
    source intensive communication, especially when our
    alternative, the serial communication, requires only one
    single wire.

2. Serial communication is simply faster. There used to be
    a time when this wasn't true, and parallel communica-
    tion was indeed faster because of the ability to send all
    data simultaneously, however that is no longer the case.
    This is due to the fact that it is easier to handle propaga-

tion time with fewer connections, there is less crosstalk to deal with than in the case of parallel communication, and we simply save resources by dealing with a smaller number of wires.

Because of these reasons, nowadays we are mostly dealing with serial communication, whether it's done through physical wires or wireless systems. This also means that there are a great number of serial protocols to be used in this communication form.

Serial Communication Types

Serial communication becomes a bit more complicated when you take a closer look at it. It can be defined in several ways, and each one holds different characteristics. With that being said, let's briefly discuss the most common types of serial communication and characteristics:

1. Synchronous serial communication: This communication form has a timer that maintains a time reference for everyone who takes part in the communication. A simple example of the synchronous serial communication is the phone.

2. Asynchronous serial communication: There is no need for information from the timer or clock to be sent through the channel. This leads to a more efficient method of communication, however there may be problems with the ability to understand the data that passes

through. For instance, texting is the perfect example of asynchronous communication.

3. Duplex mode: This is a characteristic belonging to any communication channel. It can be unidirectional, bidirectional, or bidirectional simultaneously. Unidirectional is quite self-explanatory, as the data travels only in one direction between point A and point B. Bidirectional only goes in one direction at the same time, while the simultaneous bidirectional goes both ways.

4. Peering and bus: If we have a peering system, it means that all the speakers are connected to the listeners in some way. The link can either be physical or logical. This system doesn't require a master, and usually it is asynchronous. If we have a bus system, however, everything is linked physically.

5. Masters and slaves: As you may know, when dealing with a master/slave bus structure, we simply have a master device which is connected to a number of devices which are the slaves. This system is normally synchronous, as there is a timer inside the master.

No matter the serial communication system, the main issue you will have to deal with is avoiding misunderstandings and overlaps. Luckily, there are multiple techniques that will help you fix these problems.

One of the most important things to keep in mind when working with serial communication protocols is that you need to define the word length in bits, an empty time frame, and an error detecting solution. For instance, how can you as a listener figure out when a certain word begins if we don't define these properties? These behaviors are crucial and need to be encoded into all communication participants, otherwise the communication protocol will be invalid.

Multiple Serial Protocols

In this section we are going to discuss several serial protocols and interfaces to help you better understand serial communication. Some of them have been used in the early days of computers, and many of them are still used today.

1. The telegraphy protocol: Ever heard of Morse code? Of course you have! The Morse code telegraphy protocol is an example of one of the very first serial protocols to ever be used in communications. As you may know, the way it works is by sending either short or long signals that are separated by an empty time frame. A communications operator would transmit anything from simple words, to complex data. The protocol was implemented in a system that involves only wires that transmit electrical pulses, as well as an electromagnetic wave carrier system. This type of communication can be categorized inside an asynchronous, peering or duplex system, however there are some particular rules that need to be followed. For instance, the pulse can either be long, short, or void, however there is no timer between the

two parties.

2. RS 232: This nearly 60 year old interface is still used today in many devices, especially personal computers. It is used to define the hardware used to establish connections, such as pins. The RS 232 is a point to point interface that is capable of sending data over shorter distances with great speed. Keep in mind that the speed depends on the length of the cable, as well as the type of the wire (shielded or unshielded).

3. From the 25 pin connector to 3 pins: We discussed earlier that we require a communication system capable of hardware flow control as well as error detection. The standard 25 pin connector has been used for a long time for many purposes because it offers just that, however, we can reduce its functionality to three pins. All that is needed is a wire for data transmission, for data receival, and the ground. Keep in mind that the 25 pin connector has been designed to work with many types of devices, and this is why there is such a large number of signals going through it. For example, we have pins 8 and 22 that are meant for the phone line. In this system, we have pin 7 as the ground, pin 2 as the data transmission wire, and pin 3 as the data receiving wire. This is all we need in order to establish proper communication. This three pin communication structure is something that the Arduino also replicates within its own system. In other words, the Arduino also uses a three-wire serial inter-

face. Both the Arduino Uno and Leonardo provide you with the same three wires.

4. The I2C multi-master bus: This system uses only a serial data line and a serial clock line, therefore in order to use it we have to start with the Arduino as the master and create the two wire bus. To know which wire goes where, you will have to check with Arduino's wire reference page which you can find on their website. The reason why this system is a great option for many projects is because data integrity is well maintained during the communication, and you have control over both short range communication as well as intermittent communication, all in the same system.

5. The synchronous serial peripheral interface: Also known as SPI for short, this interface has been designed by Motorola and includes four pins. There's a serial clock controlled by the master device, a master output and slave input, a master input and slave output, and slave selection. The SPI is particularly useful in projects where we have a single master and a single slave. While other options can also be used in this case, this interface provides us with far more speed than an I2C system for example. This is why it is often used to provide communication between a coder or decoder and a digital signal processor. The connection involves communicating data in and out simultaneously. Keep in mind that SPI can also be used together with I2C for

certain applications.

6. The USB: The universal serial bus is known to everyone, as no computer, laptop, or any electronic device for that matter can "live" without one nowadays. Why is it so popular? Simply because it offers a plug and play capability where other devices require you to restart your computer or perform some kind of setup. The USB was created to solve the communication problem between devices by offering a standardized connection for any kind of hardware. For instance, you can establish a large variety of connections such as audio, printer, webcam, flash drive, wireless, keyboard, etc.

Now that you know more about serial communication and how data is communicated inside the electronic components, we are going to build up on this knowledge in the next chapter, where we will discuss more about Arduino outputs.

CHAPTER 4: VISUAL OUTPUT FEEDBACK

When it comes to feedback, we obviously require interaction, as we are the ones performing various actions in a system, which in turn gives us the feedback required by us to perform other actions or modifications. Without feedback, we lack the necessary information needed to make certain adjustments to an application. So far we've mostly discussed working with the Arduino and manipulating its functions in order to achieve a specific goal. For example, in a previous chapter we communicated information to the Arduino with the use of switches and instructed it to perform a task.

An example of feedback can be found in an earlier chapter where we discuss the visualization of an action that occurs after a button press. This graphical representation of the result is in fact feedback. With that in mind, in this chapter we are going to discuss more about the development of graphical feedback systems. We are going to mainly use LED driven feedback deriving from the Arduino board. We will start by using some simple monochromatic LEDs, and advance towards LED matrices and multiplex LEDs. Finally, we are going to also have a brief introduction to LCD displays.

Using LEDs

As you already know, there are many types of LEDs such as the basic ones, OLEDs, AMOLEDs, and FOLEDs. When we refer to basic LEDs we are talking about the simple components that form an easy to take a part structure. OLEDs, for instance, are organic LEDs that include the layering of an organic semiconductor, while AMOLEDs are active matrix OLEDs that are used in large displays because they provide a densely packed number of pixels to render a quality image. For the purposes of this section, we are going to stick to the basic LEDs because there is no need to be concerned with added components. In the end, the principle is the same.

LEDs generally come in two shapes. You have the old fashioned ones with two legs sticking out, and the more modern versions that are wide surfaces with many connectors. These types of LEDs can be further broken down into monochromatic and polychromatic ones. In the case of polychromatic ones, you should take into consideration how easy it is to control which color is being powered.

In the following example, we are going to work with several LEDs, meaning several buttons as well. We already discussed using multiple switches earlier, therefore we can use that information in this scenario as well. Let's start by using the same circuit structure as earlier, but simply remove a switch and connect two LEDs in its place. As we already discussed, you can use the digital pins either as inputs or outputs. We are going to have two switches on one side connected to the 5V pin, and on the other side they will be connected to pin 2 and pin 3. We will also have a pull down type resistor connected to both 2 and 3 pins because we need to sink the current into the ground pin. Once these connections are established, you need to connect one LED to pin 8 and one to pin 9 and then ground both of them. Now before we get to the coding part, we need to discuss something known as coupling. This concept is important for any interaction design.

Coupling

You will find the information in this section to be useful in many interface designs meant for the communication between man and computer. As you should already know, the Arduino connects the control as well as the feedback sections together. This means that no matter what external force operates on the device, Arduino thinks of it as human. This is what is referred to as control-feedback coupling. It is a concept that contains a number of rules that define how the system interacts with the user and how it reacts when it sends us any kind of feedback. Let's say you would like to use the Arduino to exert your control over another system. In this case, you will have to perform the coupling outside of the Arduino.

With that being said, let's prepare a little program that includes coupling. Here are the two things we want to achieve with this exercise. By pressing the first switch, the first LED is turned on, and if the switch is released, the LED is turned off. We want the same thing to happen with a second LED. Now, in order to control some of these elements, we are going to use the "Bounce" library, which contains the tools we need to perform debouncing on the inputs. We already discussed this concept in an earlier chapter, therefore you should keep in mind that switch press needs to be smoothed out in order to filter any faulty button press detections. Now let's take a look at the following code and discuss it:

```
#include <Bounce.h>

#define BUTTON01 2    // the first button pin

#define BUTTON02 3    // the second button pin

#define LED01 8       // the first button pin

#define LED02 9       // the second button pin

//we  will have two debouncers with a debouncing time of 7 ms

Bounce bouncer_button01 = Bounce (BUTTON01, 7);

Bounce bouncer_button02 = Bounce (BUTTON02, 7);

void setup() {

    pinMode(BUTTON01, INPUT); // pin 2 input setup

    pinMode(BUTTON02, INPUT); // pin 3 input setup

    pinMode(LED01, OUTPUT);   // pin 8 output setup
```

```
    pinMode(LED02, OUTPUT);   // pin 9 output setup

}

void loop(){

    // our debouncers need to be updated

    bouncer_button01.update();

    bouncer_button02.update();

    // debounced button states

    int button01_state = bouncer_button01.read();

    int button02_state = bouncer_button02.read();

    // testing button states

    if ( button01_state == HIGH ) digitalWrite(LED01,
    HIGH);

    else digitalWrite(LED01, LOW);

    if ( button02_state == HIGH ) digitalWrite(LED02,
    HIGH);

    else digitalWrite(LED02, LOW);

}
```

As you can see, we started by including the Bounce library in the header and by defining the constants that contain our LEDs and switches. Then we instantiate the debouncers and declare a

7ms debounce time. We have chosen this value because it is enough to make the system ignore any bouncing results. Next up, we have the setup section as usual, and we declare the button's digital pins as inputs, and the LED's digital pins as outputs. As you should recall, digital pins can be either an output or an input. In the next steps, we begin a loop where we update the debouncers and record each one's value. Finally, we take control over the LEDs and instruct them how to behave depending on the state of the switches. Now the question is, where is coupling involved in all of this? This is the true last step, as the control represented by the pressed switches is coupled to the feedback represented by the LEDs.

So far we managed to successfully connect multiple LEDs (2) to the Arduino, which means that in theory we can connect as many as we want. However, what if we're using an Arduino Uno? How can we handle more than, let's say, 6 switches and 6 LEDs to match them? The answer to this question is multiplexing. Keep in mind that this concept can also be used in the case of the Arduino Mega, in case you need to connect more than, let's say, fifty LEDs and switches to it. With that being said, let's discuss how we can effectively connect a large number of LEDs and switches.

Multiplexing

The concept of multiplexing allows us to connect a large number of peripherals to the Arduino board without requiring an equally large number of inputs and outputs. In other words, we will need only a few pins to connect many external components to the board. The connection between the peripherals and the Arduino is performed with a multiplexer and demultiplexer.

To demonstrate the concept, we are going to work with an 8 bit serial-in and serial or parallel-out component. What does that mean? The control is managed through a serial interface by using the three Arduino pins, but also uses eight of its own pins. Now let's see how we can connect 8 LED lights by using only 3 pins. We are going to connect the component to a shift register first in order to multiplex 8 outputs. With that in mind, let's take a look at the actual wiring. The Arduino supplies the power for the breadboard, while the shift register uses the ground and the 5V as its power supply and configuration. In order for the Arduino to use a serial protocol and control the shift register, the component needs to be linked to pin 11, 12, and 14. Let's examine the shift register up close. In this example we are using the 74HC595 chip:

1. We have pin 8 and pin 16 that we need for the power supply.

2. Pin 10 has to be connected to the ground so that we can activate it.

3. Pin 13 also needs to be connected to the ground, as it has to be active at all times in order to drive the device's output current.

4. Next we have pin 11 as the clock input for the shift register, pin 12 as the clock input for the storage register,

pin 14 as the serial input, and pins 1 to 7 as well as pin 15 as our output pins.

In our example we are relying on pins 11, 12, and 14 for the control in order to load eight bits. The bits can then be sent serially to the device and be stored inside its register. This is what a shift register is, essentially. We simply shift bits from zero to seven as we load them.

With that being said, let's take a look at the programming side of the project. We need to use a specific design that works for this type of device. That means that for our shift register model, we need to create firmware that is specifically intended to work only with it alone. However, if we plan to use another model, the code will only require some minor modifications that are easy to make.

Now let's discuss the general design of the firmware. The first step we need to take is defining the three pins of the shift register. All three of them need to be setup as an output. This is done inside the familiar setup() section. This is how this step would look in any case similar to what we are doing:

```
digitalWrite(latch-pin, LOW)

shiftOut(data-pin, clock-pin, MSBFIRST, my_states)

digitalWrite(latch-pin, HIGH)
```

Keep in mind that this design pattern is frequently used in may shift registering operations, and you will encounter it in many other examples. Keep in mind that the storage register clock input pin (12) is what provides us with the ability to communicate with the circuit that we are going to send information through that will later be applied to the outputs. To clarify, if pin 12 is determined to have a LOW value, we are going to instruct the system to store the data we are sending. However, if it's HIGH, the data that was sent will have to go to the outputs. Next, we also need a "shiftOut" function, which will allow us to send the data to a certain pin at a certain speed in a certain transmission order. These transmission orders can either be MSB (most significant bit), or LSB (least significant bit). Before we continue, you need to first understand what these concepts mean.

Let's assume we have a byte 1 0 1 0 0 1 1 0. The most significant bit is the one at the extreme left position and having the highest value. In our example, the value would be 1. The least significant bit, on the other hand, is at the right most position and with the smallest value. In our example, the value would be 0. If we use the shift out function under these conditions, we can provide specific arguments regarding the transmission. We can either follow the MSB concept and send bits 1, followed by 0 and then 1 0 0 1 1 0, or follow the LSB concept and send bits 0 1 1 0 0 1 0 1.

Using Random Seeds

Now that you know more about the design pattern, let's discuss how we can develop a system that can generate random bytes. The bytes will be transmitted to the shift register and our array of eight LEDs will therefore have a random state. But what does random mean?

As you may already know, when it comes to computers, when we refer to random we aren't talking about something truly random. For instance, you might know about the random function, but you should also know that it is in fact a pseudo random number generator. Its more accurate name is the deterministic random bit generator, as the sequence of numbers is determined by certain established values where the seed is included. Keep in mind that numbers are generated in the same sequence for each seed. However, we have some power to influence this aspect by either forcing the seed to vary or by adding some form of randomness from an external source.

With that in mind, there is always some form or another of electronic noise interfering even if there are no wired connections. Being aware of this gives us the ability to use noise by reading the input 0. As you may already know from the previous book's analog section, we have an analogRead function which provides us with a number between 0 and 1023. We can use this in the application and define a counter variable and a byte. We can read the value that comes to the pin inside the setup method and then generate a random byte together with a bitWrite function and a loop. Then we can write every single bit of the byte by using the generated numbers from a random number function that gives us either 0 or 1 as a random result. Next, the pseudo random generated byte can be used within the same structured, however we need to redefine every seed's loop execution by reading the analog to digital conversion for pin 0.

So far we've discussed how much it would benefit us to use shift registers, as they only require a very small number of digital pins. But the question remains: what do we do if we need even more pins for a larger project? A shift register only needs three pins to power eight LEDs, but we are still limited by how many shift registers we connect. After all, we don't have an infinite number of pins to play with. The answer to this problem is daisy chaining!

Daisy Chaining

Daisy chaining is a system of wiring that is often used when we have to connect a certain number of devices together in a sequence. In this section, we are going to discuss how to use the daisy chain concept on a group of shift registers that are linked together by using the ShiftOutX library. This library can be downloaded for free from the Arduino playground section from the following link:

https://playground.arduino.cc/Main/ShiftOutX/

Now let's talk about the design. The first thing to keep in mind is that we need to communicate the serial clock, the latch, and the data throughout the chain. Serial communication needs to be synchronized with the serial clock and to instruct the shift registers that the received information needs to be stored. Any serial information that we receive from the Arduino needs to go to our first shift register, which in turn sends this data to the next one. Basically, this is how daisy chaining works.

With that being said, let's see this concept in action by examining the following code:

```
#include <ShiftOutX.h>

#include <ShiftPinNo.h>

int CLOCK_595 = 4;   // linking the first clock pin to pin 4

int LATCH_595 = 3;   // linking the first latch pin to pin 3

int DATA_595 = 2;    // linking the first serial data input pin to pin 2

int SR_Number = 2;   // declaring how many shift registers we have in the daisy chain

// enable the shiftOutX library

shiftOutX    regGroupOne(LATCH_595,    DATA_595, CLOCK_595, MSBFIRST, SR_ Number);

// our random variables

int counter = 0;
```

```
byte LED0to7_states = B00000000 ;

byte LED8to15_states = B00000000 ;

void setup() {

    // there's no need to individually prepare every single
    digital pin as earlier

    // the library takes care of everything for us

    // but we need to use a seed that comes from the noise
    of the analog to digital conversion

    randomSeed(analogRead(0)) ;

}

void loop(){

    // generating two random bytes

    for (int i = 0 ; i < 8 ; i++)

    {

        bitWrite(LED0to7_states, i, random(2));

        bitWrite(LED8to15_states, i, random(2));

    }

    unsigned long int data;

    data = LED0to7_states | (LED8to15_states << 8); // ag-
```

gregate the random bytes

```
shiftOut_16(DATA_595, CLOCK_595, MSBFIRST,
data); // send data to shift registers

// after every 5000 loop we need a new seed for the ran-
dom function

if (counter < 5000) counter++;

else

{

    randomSeed(analogRead(0));    // reading new val-
    ues from pin 0

    counter = 0; // this is a counter reset

}

// time delay before changing the LED state

delay(45);

}
```

As you may have noticed, one of the biggest differences in our firmware pattern is the way we wrote the setup section. We no longer have to declare certain arguments for our digital pins, as the new library takes care of this part automatically. However, keep in mind that earlier in the code we have passed three Arduino pins as arguments, which actually sets them up as outputs as well.

Next, we have the usual loop section which is very similar to our previous iterations. However, we are generating two random bites in this case because we need 16 values in order to set up the shiftOut_16 function which communicates all of the data in one single argument. Generating bytes and then aggregating them into an integer with the help of bitwise operators is quite a common, standard practice, however you may have had little experience with it so far, so let's discuss how it all works.

Imagine you have the following sets of 8 bits:

0 1 1 1 0 1 0 0

1 1 0 1 0 0 0 1

Now, how do we proceed in order to store them in the same location? As already discussed, we need to start by shifting one of the bits and then add it to the next one, like so:

0 1 1 1 0 1 0 0 << 8 = 0 1 1 1 0 1 0 0 0 0 0 0 0 0 0 0

But what if we perform an extra set, and use the | bitwise operator? Here's what happens:

0 1 1 1 0 1 0 0 0 0 0 0 0 0 0 0 | 1 1 0 1 0 0 0 1 = 0 1 1 1 0 1 0 0 1 1 0 1 0 0 0 1

What we have is basically a concatenation, and this is what we achieved in our code, followed by the use of the shiftOut_16 function that transmits the data to the 2 shift registers we defined in the beginning. However, at this point you might be wondering what we would do if we'd be dealing with 4 shift registers instead. The principle remains essentially the same, but we would have to increase the shift by first using << 32, then << 16, and finally << 8 so that we can store all of the bytes into a single variable. Once the process is complete, we would have a shiftOut_32 function to communicate the result.

Keep in mind that with the ShiftOutX library there can be two groups of 8 shift registers each, which means that you use as little as 4 pins to drive 128 outputs. This makes it possible for you to rely on just a single Arduino board, however you still need to consider the amount of current. If we scale our example and use 128 LED lights, all connected to the same Arduino, and we turn all of them on at the same time, we might completely ruin the board due to the amount of current. With that in mind, most devices would just reset or shut down before burning out, but in any case you don't want to try this out on your own.

An Arduino board with a USB power supply can only rely on 500 mA without encountering serious issues. Keep in mind that the total number of pins put together can only drive 200 mA, while an individual pin can handle 40 mA at best. Naturally, these figures will vary depending on the model of the board. So far in our examples we did not have to take the possibility of a short into consideration, because we used such a small amount of power to work with a limited number of devices. However, at your current skill level you may find yourself tempted to work on a bigger project that involves more juice. Let's say your LED light requires approximately 10 mA to function properly. This means that if you have an array of 8 LEDs, you will need 80mA to power everything up simultaneously with the help of a shift register. Keep in mind that if you use more shift registers, the power requirement goes up. Another factor that is often not taken into consideration is the power requirement of your integrated circuits, such as the shift register circuit or a resistor. They consume some power but it is usually negligible. However, it might be important to take it all into account if you drive your Arduino board to the limit.

Using LCDs

In this section we are going to have a brief discussion about working with Liquid Crystal Displays. This type of technology is used in nearly everything nowadays, including in watches, monitors, phones, cameras, and so on.

There are two major types of LCDs. One is based on using a character matrix and is referred to as a character LCD, and the second is based on a pixel matrix and therefore is referred to as a graphical LCD. But how do you get your hands on either of them without breaking the budget? These days you can find circuit boards with an LCD already attached to it pretty much anywhere and it won't cost you much. In most cases, you will also be lucky enough to find one with all the connectors you need to link the device to the Arduino.

The Arduino also contains a library called LiquidCrystal, and it can be used with any type of LCD. Keep in mind that the only limitation is the Hitachi HD33780 driver that is necessary, however it is extremely common and you shouldn't have to worry about it. This dedicated driver was developed to include a micro controller that makes it possible for character LCDs to connect to the outside world with the help of a 16 pin connector. With that being said, let's play around with an LCD and display some random messages with the following lines of code:

```
#include <LiquidCrystal.h>

String manyMessages[4]; int counter = 0;

// initializing the library with the number of pins in the circuit

LiquidCrystal lcd(12, 11, 5, 4, 3, 2);

void setup() {

    // LCD columns and rows

    lcd.begin(16, 2);

    manyMessages[0] = "My name is Arduino";

    manyMessages[1] = "I have the ability to communicate!";

    manyMessages[2] = "My sensors help me feel things!";
```

```
manyMessages[3] = "I am even able to react!";

// roll the dice

randomSeed(analogRead(0); }

void loop() {

// set the cursor to column 0 and row 0  lcd.setCursor(0, 0);

// 5s each

if (millis() - counter > 5000)

{

    lcd.clear(); // clear the whole LCD

    lcd.print(manyMessages[random(4)]);  // displaying a
    random message

    counter = millis();

}

    // set the cursor to column 0 and row 1

    lcd.setCursor(0, 1);

    // print the value of millis() at each loop() execution

    lcd.print("up since: " + millis() + "ms");

}
```

As usual, the first step we need to take is implementing the LiquidCrystal library into our firmware. Next, we have two variables, namely an array of strings that is needed for the message storage, and a counter that we need for time tracking. The library is then initialized and the variables are passed in such a way to fit with every pin that is required to wire an LCD to our Arduino. Keep in mind that the order of the pins is very important in this process, therefore you should go with rs, enable, d4, d5, d6, and d7. Inside the setup section, we need to use the hardware information in order to define the dimensions of the LCD. In our example we define it 16 columns and 2 rows. The next step is to store a number of messages inside the array, and then use the loop section to place our cursor on the first position of our display. In this block of code, we also check whether the following operation is true: (millis() − counter > 5000). If it is, then we can clear the entire display and then print a random message. Take note that we create a pseudo randomly generated number between zero and three, and because we are using a random index the display message will be chosen randomly from the ones we defined. Lastly, the present time is recorded in order to have a time measurement that tells us how much time passed since the previous message was displayed. The cursor is then placed on the second row, first column, and a string is printed. This string contains information on the variable that displays how much time passed since the Arduino was reset.

CHAPTER 5: MOVEMENT

So far we focused on data communication and sensors, however the Arduino can also react to movement. Whether we are talking about objects moving, or producing air movements (sound), this little board is up to the task.

In this chapter, we are going to discuss taking control of servo motors and learn how to take advantage of using transistors to manage higher amounts of current. We will also explore the area of sound generation. As the main project for this chapter, we are going to develop a synthesizer that can be controlled through MIDI. Let's get to work!

Using a Piezoelectric Sensor

One of the best ways to illustrate Arduino's versatile capabilities is to introduce you to the piezoelectric sensor, which allows us to design an object that moves with the help of the firmware we design. So far we focused on visual feedback, however keep in mind that there are other types of feedback that can be useful in many scenarios such as this one. For instance, let's say we are attaching some devices and piezoelectric sensors to a jacket. Visual LED feedback wouldn't be useful for this project, however we can send feedback to the person wearing the jacket by using vibrations. With these sensors on either side of the jacket, we can send feedback in different forms depending on what kind of interaction the wearer is performing.

The piezoelectric sensor is a device that relies on the piezoelectric effect, as the name suggests. This effect can be defined as a linear electromechanical communication between an electrical state and a mechanical state in certain objects. In other words, the mechanical action generates the electricity and therefore it can be used for vibration or movement detection. However, if we supply the power to the object, it vibrates and therefore it is perfect for our little project. We essentially use the sensor as a way to generate vibrations. On a side note, because of these characteristics, the piezoelectric sensor is frequently used as a tone generator, however we're going to save this fact for later when we are going to discuss more about sound in particular.

In case you are worried about power consumption, a piezoelectric sensor rarely needs more than 15 mA, which your Arduino can easily deal with. However, in case of a more complex project, you should always check the official document behind the device you are using in order to make accurate calculations. In our project, we are going to use a generic piezoelectric sensor that has only two legs and is connected to the Arduino through a digital pin capable of pulse width modulation, or PWM. In case you don't recall, the reason why we are relying on PWM is because for this project we need to mimic an analog output current by using digital means. The general idea is to use the analogWrite function in order to feed the sensor with different voltages. With that being said, let's take a look at our code for generating vibrations and discuss the technical side of the project.

```
int piezoPin = 9;

int value = 0;  // storing the value of the feed

int incdec = 1; // storing the variation's direction

void setup() {

}

void loop() {

//checking the value of the current and changing the variation's direction if needed

    if (value == 0 || value == 255) incdec *= -1;

    analogWrite(piezoPin, value + incdec);

    delay(30);

}
```

As you can see, the analogWrite function fulfills the purpose of taking the digital pin as a value, as well as an argument. The value goes from 0 to 255 and it takes the place of an analog output by mimicking it. We use the function with the increment / decrement parameter in order to store an increment value for every single loop that is carried out. This value will change whenever it reaches one of its limits, whether it's 0 or 255, and then it inverts itself. This is a simple method of forcing the cycle to keep going from 0 to 255 and then the other way around, without requiring any resource intensive operations. Basically, this code controls the sensor by making it vibrate from a lower, less intensive value to a higher setting.

Now that we covered a simple movement control example, let's proceed with a more advanced project where we discuss how to manipulate larger, more complex motors.

Transistors

Before we move on to more complicated motors, we need to take a side step and discuss more about transistors. So far in previous chapters we have mentioned them, and used them as digital switches. Keep in mind that they are incredibly versatile, and therefore can be used as a way to stabilize voltages or in place of amplifiers. Because of their frequent use, you can find these little devices everywhere and you won't have to break the bank to acquire them.

In case you need a reminder, a typical transistor has three legs, namely the base, an emitter, and a collector. Now, if we flood the base of the transistor by attaching a power supply to it, with 5 V worth of current, all of the power that comes from the collector will be sent through the emitter. This makes the transistor an excellent device for controlling the large amount of energy that the Arduino cannot drive on its own. Keep in mind that when the transistor is used in this manner, the Arduino can control it simply because such a tiny power supply is required by the base of the transistor.

Understanding this design pattern is important for the projects we are going to discuss, as well as for many projects you might pursue on your own in the future. Keep in mind that having an external power supply is often needed, and recommended, when working with motors. With that being said, let's apply what we discussed to the practical application of servo motors.

Using Servomotors

As you probably already know, a servomotor is characterized by a rotary actuator that provides us with the ability to fine tune an angular position. Servos are widely used in many technologies and nowadays can be found at a very low cost pretty much everywhere. When purchasing one for your robotics projects, you should keep in mind that not all of them are equal, meaning that some require a great deal of power. Why is this important in our case? We are working with an Arduino, and powerful servomotors require a stronger supply than the board can provide. In translation, you would only be able to use one servo or two at most, unless you use an external power supply.

When do we use servomotors? Whenever your project demands the ability to control an object's position based on its rotation angle. Servomotors aren't needed only for making various components turn or rotate inside your robot. They can also be used to move the entire object. This is how most Arduino robot projects are built, and you can find many examples of them if you do a quick search. For instance, a servomotor would often be attached to the arm or leg of a machine where another component will be attached from the other side of the device. Imagine the servo as a joint that offers mobility. So how do we take care of the technical aspect of working with servomotors?

Luckily, Arduino provides us with an extensive library that contains everything we could possibly need. This library is appropriately called Servo, and it allows us to use a maximum number of 12 servomotors on typical Arduino boards, and up to 48 if we're using a Mega board. For now we are going to presume that we have access only to a simple board in order to work out what kind of design limitations we have to face. An example of such a limitation is the fact that pins 9 and 10 won't work with the analogWrite method we used earlier.

Keep in mind that most servomotors come in a 3 pin package containing the ground, pulse, and 5V. Basically, we have the control pin, however the pulse will be the board and as a power supply we are going to use an external source such as a battery. With that being said, let's take a look at the code behind the design of an application that provides us with cyclical movement between 0 and 180 degrees.

```
#include <Servo.h>
```

```
Servo myServo;

int angle = 0;  // current angle

void setup() {

   myServo  myServo.attach(9);

}

void loop() {

   for(angle = 0; angle < 180; angle += 1)

   {

       myServo.write(angle);

       delay(20);

   }

   for(angle = 180; angle >= 1; angle -=1)

   {

       myServo.write(angle);

       delay(20);

   }

}
```

As always, we start by including the required library and by instantiating the object, in this example being myServo. Inside the setup section we first need to connect the servo object to pin 9 and therefore define the pin as the control for myServo. Next up, we have the loop section where we declare 2 "for" loops in the same fashion as previously done in our piezoelectric sensor example. A cycle is defined where the angle is incremented progressively from 0 to 180 degrees and then decremented backwards. We also added a 20 ms delay in-between the cycles. Lastly, we have the Servo.read function which reads the present angle of the device. This operation is required in case we want to perform some dynamic changes without storing the values every single time.

Multiple Servomotors

Now that you know the basics behind working with one servomotor, let's discuss what it takes to use more of them simultaneously. For most projects there isn't much you can do with one motor, therefore you should know the intricacies behind operating multiple ones.

With that being said, let's consider using three motors. As already mentioned, servomotors simply perform the operation of converting power to movement, therefore the more of them we use, the more current we need to manage. Provided you are using your Arduino connected to a PC, the power supply provided through the USB connection is only enough as long as you don't go over 500 mA. For anything more than that, you need an external power source. This means that when using three servomotors or more, you will need to use either a power supply adapter connected to your wall socket or batteries. In this example we are going to use the classic AA batteries. Don't forget that you can always use batteries to simply power your board and thus gain some freedom of movement without being forced to be connected to a stationary computer.

Keep in mind that when using batteries in this way, we have to wire all of our grounds together. We can do this simply because the batteries will be our only power supply for the motors and nothing else. Now let's dive straight into the code and see how we can control the three servomotors:

```
#include <Servo.h>

Servo servo01;

Servo servo02;

Servo servo03;

int angle;

void setup() {

    servo01.attach(9);

    servo02.attach(10);

    servo03.attach(11);

}
```

```
void loop()

{

    for(angle = 0; angle < 180; angle += 1)

{

    servo01.write(angle);

    servo02.write(135-angle/2);

    servo03.write(180-angle);

    delay(15);

}

}
```

The code is quite self-explanatory, and you shouldn't have trouble understanding it. The servomotors are instantiated and every one of them is connected to its own pin inside the setup section. Then we have the loop block, where we handle the angles by defining an angle variable. As in earlier examples, the variables goes into a repeating cycle from 0 to 180 degrees, and the motor that is connected to pin 9 is driven with the value obtained from the variable. The second motor that is connected to pin 10, however, is driven with a value that goes from 135 to 45 degrees. The third motor is then driven with an angle value of 180 degrees, which as you may notice is the opposite movement of the first motor.

The firmware we wrote is the perfect example of how to control a single variable, while also being able to build variations around it. In our example we have varied angle values and we also create different variable combinations depending on the expression. Now, keep in mind that this isn't the only approach you can take to solve the problem on using multiple servos. We can also control the motor's position with the help of an outside parameter. For instance, we can use the measured distance or the potentiometer's position. With that being said, we are going to extend some of these concepts in the next section where we are going to discuss stepper motors.

Stepper Motors

Sometimes called step motors, these devices can be controlled through small steps, as the name suggests. The rotation of the motor is split in equal steps, therefore the position of the motor can be held at any of these steps. This is done accurately and without the need of any kind of feedback system. The control over the movement is asserted either forward or backward by manipulating the step sequence. The Arduino is extremely capable of handling the entire process, and that is why stepper motors are a great addition to your project toolkit. With that being said, let's discuss in more detail the unipolar stepper motors.

Also referred to as unipolar steppers, these motors are built using a central shaft and 4 electromagnetic coils. The reason they are called unipolar is because they only use the current that comes through a single pole. Keep in mind that in a similar way to the servomotors, it is recommended that you control the stepper motor with an external power supply. The best option in this case, however, is to use the wall adapter instead of AA batteries. All you need to do is take pins 5 and 6 and send some power through them. The next step you need to take is using the board to control pins 1, 2, 3, and 4 with the help of a Darlington transistor array such as the ULN 2004 or ULN 2003 devices. In case you don't know, a Darlington array is used to achieve high power amplification by boosting the current from the first transistor with the second transistor and so on. In our case the ULN2004 would be better suited because it can handle up to 15 V of power, while the ULN2003 is at 5V only.

When working with a stepper motor, we need to have control over extremely accurate movements, and in order to achieve this we need to know certain sequences which can be found only in the device's datasheet. The sequences table would look something like this one:

Step	A	B	C	D
1	HIGH	HIGH	LOW	LOW
2	LOW	HIGH	HIGH	LOW
3	LOW	LOW	HIGH	HIGH
4	HIGH	LOW	LOW	HIGH

The idea is that if we plan to perform a rotation clockwise, we need a sequence going from step 1 to 4 and back to 1 again. This is done cyclically over and over again. If you need to perform a counterclockwise rotation, you simply need to generate the opposite sequence. But how do we handle all of this through code without writing a large number of sequences? Luckily, there's a function for that inside the adequately named Stepper library which is part of the Arduino. With that being said, let's take a look at the following code:

```
#include <Stepper.h>

#define STEPS 200

// we need a stepper instance

Stepper stepper(STEPS, 8, 9, 10, 11);

int counter = 0; // storing the number of steps that occurred
since the last direction shift

int multiplier = 1;

void setup() {

    stepper.setSpeed(30); // 30 RPM speed

}

void loop() {

// random movement from at least one step

    stepper.step(multiplier);
```

// count the number of steps that were moved

// reset the counter and switch direction once an entire turn is reached

```
if (counter < STEPS)  counter++ ;

else {

    counter = 0;

    multiplier *= -1;

}

}
```

Once we prepare the Stepper library, we have to define how many steps are there in one rotation. If we take a look in the stepper's datasheet, we will see that the first step is represented by a 1.8 degree angle and with only a 5% margin of error. Keep in mind that this value will differ based on the model of your stepper motor, so make sure to check and change the value accordingly. Now, because the error is so small, we can consider it as a negligible factor and ignore it entirely. Therefore, we only take the 1.8 degree value into consideration. Knowing this number, we can calculate how many steps we need in order to perform a full rotation. The answer is 200 steps, as 200 * 1.8 = 360. The next step is to instantiate the stepper object with 5 specific arguments, the four Arduino pins that are connected to the device, and the step value needed for a full rotation. Before we continue, we also need a variable that handles the rotation change, and another that handles the tracing.

Next up, we have the setup section where we define the speed that actually drives the motor. We declared a value of 30 rounds per minute, which can always be modified inside the loop section if the circumstances change for various reasons. In the loop block, we push the motor to a value that is equal to a multiplier which for starters is set to 1. In other words, whenever the loop method is executed, the motor will rotate from the 1.8 degrees step clockwise. When we perform the test, we check for every round of completed steps that translate to a full rotation. As soon as we determine that we've reached rotation limit, the counter is reset and the multiplier is inverted, therefore the motor can continue in the opposite direction.

What we discussed so far can be labeled as design patterns. They can be useful in a variety of situations, so make sure to take note of them as they may give you an idea for a cheap solution that is light on resources.

Sound

As already mentioned, this chapter's main focus is movement, so why are we discussing sound? Just ask yourself: what is sound if not an air movement that produces audible data? In this section, we are going to discuss this topic because the Arduino can make the air move, just as well as it can make a robot move. Keep in mind that this will not be a complete guide to sound, but you will learn the most important topics and concepts behind working with sound. This is the beauty of developing projects with an Arduino. It is an incredibly versatile device that can perform a vast number of tasks, so let's dig in!

The simplest way to think of sound is as a mechanical wave that oscillates and can pass through various materials, whether gas, liquid, or solid. We can broaden this explanation by looking at sound as the result of these transmitted waves once it hits the human ear. When you look at it this way, you can conclude that the ears are somewhat complicated sensors that detect changes in air pressure. Our "sensors" are able to detect the movement of air (sound amplitude) and the variations in the air movements (sound frequency). Now keep in mind that all of this data from these processes is transmitted and received in real time, whether we're discussing the mixture of lower sound frequencies or higher. A certain sound can include a number of various frequencies. Our perception of sound is the summary of a number of frequencies that have certain amplitude.

As you can see, we can describe sound in several ways, however there are two general representations of it that we should consider in our Arduino projects. We are either discussing an amplitude variation over a certain amount of time, which can be represented through visual methods such as graphs, or an amplitude variation that depends on what the frequency contains. With this in mind, if your project ever requires you to convert from one representation to the other, there's a mathematical operation that does just that. It is called the Fourier

Transform, and it provides you with efficient and accurate calculations.

Now, let's take an example of the most basic type of sound wave, which is the sinusoidal air pressure variation. Let's first discuss the time domain representation of it, which is the amplitude variation over time we mentioned above. In this representation, we are looking at a cyclical sound variation with a period of time which is equal to the wavelength. What exactly is this period we're referring to? It represents the amount of time it takes for one oscillation cycle to be completed. In other words, if we manage to define the sound variation over a certain period of time, we can illustrate the visual representation of sound. Now, if we discuss the sound that originates from a specific source, the variation over a period of time will be the equivalent of the air pressure's variation. By creating a graphical interpretation of this process, we can observe the direction of the axis that matches the so called "high pressure front," which is a section of the curve represented by the time period axis. What this basically means is that we are dealing with a high pressure which presses against the inside of the human ear. Once this curve goes under zero, we are dealing with a pressure that is lower than the ambient pressure. The human ear will detect this difference.

On the other hand, when we are looking into the frequency domain representation, the graphical interpretation is seen as a simple vertical line. Keep in mind that in the time domain representation we have a graph with a pulse-like structure that illustrates the sound frequency. This visualization can be summarized with the following equation: $T = 1 / f$. In this formula, the time period is measured in seconds and represented by the T symbol, while f is the frequency which as you know is measured in Hertz. A higher frequency level leads to a higher pitched sound, and lower frequency leads to the opposite, which is a lower pitched sound. Another thing to keep in mind is that a higher frequency will also involve a much faster vibration performed over a short period of time.

Let's take a look at microphones and speakers for a moment. A microphone is a sensitive sensor that is capable of detecting extremely subtle changes in air pressure. This means that they work by simply translating these oscillations or vibrations into shifts in voltage. A speaker, on the other hand, has a mobile section which works in a similar way to the human ear in the sense that it can push or pull air. This results in vibrations, and therefore sound. The movement is achieved with the shifts in voltage. Both of these devices rely on a special membrane, while the microphone also has an electrical transducer which is necessary in order to perform air pressure changes that eventually translate to electrical signals. The speaker works by modifying electrical signals, and this process results in a pressure change. Keep in mind that both of these devices involve analog signals, and not digital.

We mentioned earlier a sound source, and we need to elaborate on this. You should take note that not all sound sources are the same. For instance, you register a sound by knocking on a piece of wood. This would be referred to as analog sound, because you perform a physical action that makes the material vibrate, thus causing oscillations in the air pressure around it. Those oscillations are then detected by your ear. On the other hand, we could be using some kind of digital device. This, however, leads to hardware limitations, and therefore we'll have difficulties making an analog description.

With that being said, we have covered some of the fundamentals behind sound and frequencies. It may seem like we briefly strayed from this chapter's topic, however it is important for you to understand the basic theory behind a concept before you actually pursue building an Arduino project. Now let's explore the concept of digitizing sound and then learn how to use the Arduino board to read and write audio signals.

Digitizing Sound

Let's say we have a system that samples the voltage variations that occur inside a microphone. When we discuss sampling we are referring to the technique of sampling and holding, which means that our system reads the analog data regularly during set time intervals. The value is received and then placed on hold until a new value is received. This is the sampling rate which is used to describe sampling frequency. With a low rate, the analog signal result is also lower, but if there's a high rate the signal is higher as well. Now, keep in mind that there is a limit that we need to take into consideration. This limit is referred to as the Nyquist frequency.

The sampling system requires the sampling to be performed at double the highest frequency inside the signal. This results in a higher accuracy and precision rate, however the downside is that we also end up with a much larger file that requires more storage. However, there is more to this process.

Another thing worth taking note is the bit depth. When working with digital devices, we required a bit-based system that represents the value of the amplitude. The bit depth can be defined as the outcome of the amplitude going from -1 to 1. The basic idea is that with a higher bit depth value we can record more using a digital system. With a lower bit depth the result would be a lower sound quality that simply doesn't contain a great deal of subtleties. For instance, let's say we have a bit depth of 0.5 to 0.7. In this scenario, we would lose the variation that resulted from the value in-between, which is 0.6. The result would either be 0.5 or 0.7, thus losing sound subtlety.

Keep in mind that both the bit depth and the sampling relies on what we need them for. The final rendering determines our purpose, which in turn determines the quality standard we have to use. There are mainly two such standards. One is the CD quality at 44.1 kHz and 16-bit, and the other is DAT at 48 kHz and 16-bit. Other options include 96kHz and 24 bits, frequently used by various sound recording studios, and 16 kHz and 8 bits used by certain enthusiasts that are looking for an old fashioned sound.

With that being said, let's talk more about the process of going from analog to digital. As you may have already guessed, this is handled by the analog to digital converter that we mentioned several times in this book as well as in the previous one. Keep in mind, however, that in order to perform a proper conversion we required good quality sound from the start, otherwise the quality will suffer significantly. The entire process is handled the same way as the Arduino already does when working with an analog input. The analog to digital converter is at 10 bits and will read the value in 111 ms intervals, which translates to a sampling rate of 9 kHz. During this process several buffers are needed to smoothen everything out.

Keep in mind that this entire process can also be performed in reverse. A digital sound can be converted to an analog sound with, you guessed it, a digital to analog converter. Data is sent by the processor into the converter as a set of values, which are then transformed into an electrical signal, and therefore analog sound.

Producing Sounds with Arduino

Now that we've covered the basic concepts behind sound, we can start involving the Arduino in producing or listening to sounds. As you already know, the board can write and read both digital as well as analog signals, meaning it can also process audio signals. On top of this functionality, we can also connect various components to improve the process further. For instance, we can use an analog to digital converter or a digital to analog converter to store the sounds. Nowadays, it's common to rely on hardware to control the firmware, and this allows us to use the Arduino as a starting point to build a collection of various controls that we then interface with our computer's software. The Arduino board can also be used to trigger sound, by transforming it into a sequencer that produces MIDI messages to a connected audio synthesizer. With that being said, let's start discussing more about sound related techniques that are specific to Arduino.

As you already know, we need two components in order to play a sound, namely an audio source and a speaker. In case you aren't yet familiar with all of Arduino's subtle intricacies, you should be aware that the board can produce on its own 8 kHz / 8-bit sounds when connected to a computer's speakers. We can use the tone function that is provided by the Arduino in order to perform an operation referred to as bit banging. We have to manipulate the board's pins in such a way so they don't hinder the pulse width modulation output from pins 3 and 11 and then toggle the input and output pins at a certain frequency.

Now let's take a look at some code where we'll use sound frequencies to create some "music" instead of actual tones.

```
void setup() {

// we require a pseudo random number generator

randomSeed(analogRead(0)) ;

}
```

```
void loop() {

    // we need to generate a pitch and duration, both of
    them being random

    int pitch = random(30,5000);

    int duration = 1000 / (random(1000) + 1);

    // playing a tone to pin 8

    tone(8, pitch, duration);

    // add a pause

    delay(duration * 1.30);

    // stop the sound

    noTone(8);

}
```

Now let's go step by step through the code and discuss the entire process. The first step is to implement a pseudo random number generator and then generate two numbers inside the loop block. First, we have the pitch with a value between 30 and 4,999, which represents the sound frequency. Secondly, we have the sound duration which is measured with a value between 1 microsecond to 1 second. Both of these arguments are needed for our tone function to be properly implemented. Once this step is achieved, we call the function and pass the pin which feeds the speaker, as an argument. A frequency wave is then generated. At this point you need to keep in mind that the sound will continue for as long as we don't call the noTone function. This is why we need to define a certain duration. The result of this code, as mentioned, is an 8-bit "song" with pseudo randomly generated tones.

CHAPTER 6: ADVANCED TECHNIQUES

Now that we've discussed a number of new individual techniques which you can apply to your Arduino projects, we can start discussing certain concepts that can either be implemented on their own or in combination with what you've learned so far. Intermediary level, and later advanced, projects will require a great deal from you. Simple techniques will not be enough to finish a real world project, therefore you need to start learning some of the more subtle concepts that complement your work.

In this chapter we are going to explore new tools and concepts that will aid you in your future Arduino projects. You will learn how to work with components such as the electrically erasable programmable read-only memory (EEPROM for short), how to use GPS modules, and how to improve the autonomy of your board. Let's get started!

Improved Data Storage

So far we've only worked with devices that are entirely dependent on power from the Arduino in order to function as programmed. This means that once there is no more current flowing through the component, all of the data and information that we gather is lost and we need to start over. Keep in mind that this doesn't mean that your actual firmware is deleted and you need to rewrite it. So, how do we solve this problem?

Most Arduino boards have three different memory types, namely the flash memory, static RAM, and EEPROM. All of these memories have their own purpose. The firmware you code is stored inside the flash memory. When the programming takes over and reads, writes, and handles variables and functions, all of this data is stored inside the static random access memory. The electrically erasable programmable read-only memory, on the other hand, is what we need in order to store something for long periods of time. From this type of memory nothing will be deleted once you turn the board off.

With that being said, let's take a look at how we can write and read using the EEPROM library. We are going to go through some code that reads all the bytes inside the memory and then prints the results.

```
#include <EEPROM.h>

// the first byte (0) is where we start reading from the
memory

int address = 0;

byte value;

void setup() {
```

```
// open port

    Serial.begin(9600);

}
void loop() {

    // use the present address to read a byte

            value = EEPROM.read(address);

    Serial.print(address);

    Serial.print("\t");

    Serial.print(value, DEC);

    Serial.println();

    // continue in order with the next address

    address = address + 1;

    // we have 512 bytes inside the memory

    // when we reach address 512, we wrap around back to 0

if (address == 512)

    address = 0;

    delay(500);

}
```

Now let's go through the code line by line and understand what's happening. The first thing we do is instantiating the

EEPROM library. Then we follow up with the variable definition that represents our ability to store a currently read address.
This variable needs to be initialized at 0 as this is the start of
the memory register. Keep in mind that the variable needs to be
defined as a byte data type. Next up, we have the setup section
where we need to initialize the serial communication, followed
by the loop section where we store the current address. The result is then printed to a serial port. Take note that in the Seri-
al.print("\t") line we are talking about tabulation, which means
that we are writing the data in such a way to make it readable
and easy to understand. Next, we move on to the next address
where we perform a verification process to see whether it is
equal to 512. If the result is checked as true, the address counter is reset to 0 and the process continues until the value of 512
is reached again. In this function we also add a short delay.

Now that we've gone through the basic process, let's discuss
more about external EEPROM connections. These memory
storage devices are widely available on the market and they are
fairly cheap. Whenever you consider that your project might
benefit from relying on this type of storage, don't hesitate to
purchase it due to budget restrictions. With that being said, we
are going to take a look at an EEPROM model that uses I2C to
perform all reading and writing operations. The 24LC256 is
one such model, and it provides us with a handy amount of
memory space of 32 kilobytes. If you require more memory,
you can also opt for its big brother, the 24LC1025, which also
relies on I2C and has a storage capability of 1024 kilobytes.
Now let's take a closer look at what makes this EEPROM tick.

We have the chip address inputs labeled as A0, A1 and A2, followed by 5V connection and the ground pin. We also have write protect pin, or WP for short. This means that if we connect it to the ground, we can still write to the memory storage, however if we connect it to the 5V pin it won't work. Next up, we have two other connections that are part of the I2C communication, namely the serial data line and the serial clock line. You need to pay particular attention to these wires, as the connection will differ based on the type of your Arduino board. Always make sure to check the documentation before you proceed with making the connections. For example, the Arduino Mega2560 has the serial data line under pin 20 and the serial clock line under pin 21, while the Arduino Leonardo has them under pin 2, and pin 3, respectively.

With that in mind, let's talk about the firmware. We are going to need to work with the "Wire" library, which handles our I2C communication requirements. This library is available straight from the Arduino and it can handle raw bits, among other things. Now let's see how to use this library and then discuss the code:

```
#include <Wire.h>

void eepromWrite(byte address, byte source_addr, byte data) {

    Wire.beginTransmission(address);

    Wire.write(source_addr);
```

```
    Wire.write(data);

    Wire.endTransmission();

}

byte eepromRead(int address, int source_addr) {

Wire.beginTransmission(address);

Wire.write(source_addr);

Wire.endTransmission();

Wire.requestFrom(address, 1);

if(Wire.available())

return Wire.read();

else

return 0xFF;

}

void setup() {

    Wire.begin();

    Serial.begin(9600);

    for(int i = 0; i < 10; i++) {

        eepromWrite(B01010000, i, 'a'+i);
```

```
        delay(100);

    }

    Serial.println("Bytes written to external EEPROM !");

}
void loop() {

    for(int i = 0; i < 10; i++) {

        byte val = eepromRead(B01010000, i);

        Serial.print(i);

        Serial.print("\t");

        Serial.print(val);

        Serial.print("\n");

        delay(1000);

    }

}
```

Once we import the library we need, we have to define the write function and the read function. Their purpose is to read and write the bytes from our external memory storage system with the help of the Wire library. The next step is to instantiate both the wire and the serial communication inside the setup section of our code and then use a "for" loop that determines how we write the information to a certain address. We specified that this information is in fact the character "a," followed by a number. What does this mean exactly? For instance, when we write the state, we can have the character "a" + 9 which results in character "j". Keep in mind that the purpose of this example is to demonstrate how easily and efficiently we can store data, even if it may not be extremely meaningful or valuable. In the next step, we print a message to the serial display which informs us that the writing process has been finished and the information is now stored inside the EEPROM. Then we have the loop section of the code where we read from the storage system.

There are a few things you need to keep in mind when working with the Wire library. Firstly, it handles two bits, namely the start bit and the acknowledge bit. Secondly, we have the chip select bits which can be modified by simply rewiring the A0, A1, and A2 pins to the ground wire, as well as the +V wire. This translates to eight different address variations that go from zero to seven. In binary they look like this: 1 0 1 0 0 0 0, 1 0 1 0 0 0 1, with the eighth address being 1 0 1 0 1 1 1. The first address is translated as 0 x 50 while the last one is translated as 0 x 57. In our example we wired the three aforementioned pins to the ground, and then the memory storage system's address becomes 0 x 50 when using the I2C bus. This doesn't mean that we have to use only one bus, however it isn't necessary unless we require a higher amount of storage space. With this information, you can now use the EEPROM's storage capacity to store anything you want, whether it's audio data, lookup tables, or simply any kind of information that requires more room than the Arduino provides you with by default.

Working with GPS Modules

In this section, we are going to focus on using modules specifically designed for projects that require the implementation of a global positioning system.

As you probably already know, GPS works by having a receiver that registers signals communicated by a minimum of four satellites. Each one of them has an atomic clock installed, which is used to calculate the propagation time of the signals and perform a precise calculation of a 3D position. As challenging as this may sound to some, it is pure trigonometry, however we are not going to dive into more mathematical details as they aren't necessary for the purpose of this section. Our goal is to parse data that originates from various GPS modules.

With that being said, let's take a look at the Parallax GPS receiver which provides the Arduino with the ability to detect a position without requiring a large amount of resources.

The Parallax GPS Receiver Module

This module provides us either with raw NMEA 01823 strings, or certain data that is requested by the user from a serial command interface. NMEA 01823 is a combination of electrical and data specifications that are required for the communication between various electronic devices such as sonars, autopilot systems, and GPS receivers. It works by using ASCII communication protocols that determine how information is transmitted from a transmitter to a listener.

With that being said, the parallax receiver module has the ability to track up to 12 satellites, as well as WAAS, which is a system that helps with the signal calculations. On a side note, WAAS is a system specific to the USA. The module itself provides us with various parameters such as the current time, date, latitude, longitude, altitude, speed, heading, and a lot more. This means that we can write data that requests certain strings from the module, however keep in mind that some of them are automatically transmitted. Here are some of these strings:

1. Global Positioning System Fix Data - $GPGGA

2. GPS satellites in view - $GPGSV

3. GPS DOP and active satellites - $GPGSA

4. Recommended minimum specific GPS data - $GPRMC

All of this data needs to be extracted by our Arduino board and then placed into application. Now let's take a brief look at the wiring behind this module. The receiver requires one single data pin, namely pin 0. At this point you might recall that we discussed earlier how we can't use the USB port for any kind of serial monitor at the same time as pins 0 and 1 are used for various serial features. Our serial implementation is full duplex when it comes to serial communication that relies on pins 0 and 1. In our example, the module would transmit data to the board through digital pin 0, which would also be connected to the USB Rx pin. Then the USB Tx pin would be used to transmit data to the computer when wired to digital pin 1. While this communication method works perfectly in our scenario, we have to also take the possibility of interferences into consideration. We do not want to transmit data from the computer to the board by using the USB. Why? Because we will encounter problems due to the fact that the USB is already busy receiving data from the module by being connected to pin 0.

When working with this module we will need to implement the serial.write function in order to write data to pin 1. Keep in mind that at this point the USB Tx pin is not connected to anything else. This means that we can transmit data to the USB without any kind of issues. Then we use the serial.read function to read from pin 0 as well as the USB. Just keep in mind that we will not transmit any kind of data from the computer to the USB. This is important in order to read from pin 0 with no risks involved. The final step we can take is pulling the /RAW pin set to low mode so that the module extracts data from the board without the user being forced to request it manually.

Parsing Data

Before we start creating our software implementation, there is one more step we need to take. We cannot take advantage of the data extracted from the GPS module without knowing what this device can transmit. In this case, you should first examine the device's datasheet in order to fully understand what you are dealing with. To make things easier for you, using the device we discussed earlier, here's an example of the type of information that we can transmit:

1. $GPRMC: this is what defines the kind of data sequence we can transmit and also includes the UTC time to fix.

2. 220516: This is the data status, which includes either a valid position or a warning.

3. A: This represents the latitude of the positional fix.

4. 5133.82: This refers to the north or south latitudes.

5. N: This is the longitude of the positional fix.

6. 00042.24: This represents the east or west longitudes.

7. W: This is the speed measured in knots.

8. 173.8: This is tracking measured in degrees.

9. 231.8: This is the UTC date of the positional fix.

10. 130694: This represents the magnetic variation and it is measured in degrees.

11. 004.2: This is the eastern or western magnetic variation.

12. W*70: This is a checksum, which is a digit that repre-

sents the sum of correct digits inside any kind of transmitted data. The purpose of this is to check for any kind of errors that may appear during the transmission process.

With information on the type of data we can transmit, now we can start coding the parser which is needed for the software component. Let's take a look at the code and then discuss it:

```
int rxPin = 0;  // This is our Rx pin or pin 0

int byteGPS = -1; // Current read byte

char line[300] = ""; // Buffer

char commandGPR[7] = "$GPRMC"; // Message related string

int counter=0;

int correctness=0;

int lineCounter=0;

int index[13];

void setup() {

    pinMode(rxPin, INPUT);

    Serial.begin(4800);

    // We need to clear the buffer
```

```
    for (int i=0;i<300;i++){

    line[i]=' ';

    }

}

void loop() {

    byteGPS = Serial.read();

    // Test whether the port is clear

    if (byteGPS == -1) {

        delay(100);

    }

    // if the port isn't clear

    else {

        line[lineCounter] = byteGPS; // the read data goes
        into the buffer

        lineCounter++;

        Serial.print(byteGPS);    // the read data is then
        printed to the serial monitor

    // We need to verify that the transmission has ended

    // If it's finished we start parsing the data
```

```
if (byteGPS==13){

    counter=0;

    correctness=0;
```

// We need to check if the command we received starts with $GPR

// If it does, then the correctness counter is increased

```
    for (int i=1;i<7;i++){

        if (line[i]==commandGPR[i-1]){

            correctness++;

        }

    }

    if(correctness==6){

        for (int i=0;i<300;i++){
```

// store position of "," separators

```
if (line[i]==','){

    index[counter]=i;

    counter++;

}
```

```
// store position of "*" separator
    if (line[i]=='*'){   // ... and the "*"
        index[12]=i;
        counter++;
    }
}
// Write data to serial monitor on the computer
Serial.println("");
Serial.println("");
Serial.println("--------------");
for (int i=0;i<12;i++){
    switch(i){
    case 0 :
        Serial.print("Time in UTC (HhMmSs): ");
        break;
    case 1 :
        Serial.print("Status (A=OK,V=KO): ");
        break;
```

```
case 2 :

    Serial.print("Latitude: ");

    break;

case 3 :

    Serial.print("Direction (N/S): ");

    break;

case 4 :

    Serial.print("Longitude: ");

    break;

case 5 :

    Serial.print("Direction (E/W): ");

    break;

case 6 :

    Serial.print("Velocity in knots: ");

    break;

case 7 :

    Serial.print("Heading in degrees: ");

    break;
```

```
        case 8 :

            Serial.print("Date UTC (DdMmAa): ");

            break;

        case 9 :

            Serial.print("Magnetic degrees: ");

            break;

        case 10 :

            Serial.print("(E/W): ");

            break;

        case 11 :

            Serial.print("Mode: ");

            break;

        case 12 :

            Serial.print("Checksum: ");

            break;

        }
        for (int j=index[i];j<(index[i+1]-1);j++){

            Serial.print(line[j+1]);
```

```
        }
        Serial.println("");
    }
    Serial.println("---------------");
    }
// Reset the buffer
lineCounter=0;
for (int i=0;i<300;i++){
line[i]=' ';
}
}
}
}
```

At this point you might feel a bit confused, but don't worry, we're going to discuss every operation we performed with this code. Let's first "decipher" the variables because we have quite a few of them. Here they are:

1. rxPin: This variable represents the digital input to which the module is connected. Also known as digital pin 0.

2. byteGPS: This variable is simply the most current byte read that comes from the device. Keep in mind we are using serial communication.

3. line: This is our buffer array.

4. commandGPR: We need to parse messages, and this is a string variable that does precisely that.

5. counter: This is simply the index of the index array.

6. correctness: This variable is used to store the validity of the messages.

7. lineCounter: We need this variable in order to keep track of the data's buffer position.

8. index: This variable stores the position of GPS's string separators.

Now that we've gotten that out of the way, let's start discussing the firmware in more detail. As always, we have a setup block where we define the Rx pin (pin 0) as our input, in order to begin the serial communication. The communication is performed at a rate of 4800 baud. If you take a look at the parallax receiver's datasheet, you will see that this rate is a requirement for the serial interface. On a side note, baud is a measurement unit used in telecommunications, as well as electronics, and it represents the speed of the communication over a certain data channel. Always examine your datasheet to make sure you follow all of your device's requirements, otherwise the code won't work as desired. The last part of the setup section also includes a clearing of the line array buffer. This operation is performed by simply filling the buffer with a space character.

Next, we have our usual loop section where we start by reading the byte from digital pin 0. Keep in mind that if the port contains something, we skip to the else block. However, if the port is empty, we simply wait for a period of 100ms before attempting to read it again. The parsing process starts by placing the data inside the buffer at the index of the lineCounter array. Once this operation is underway we need to start incrementing the index in order to properly store any data we receive. The read data is then printed in a raw line to the USB port, allowing us to display it as raw data to the serial monitor. Once we have the data, we verify it by comparing it to 13 and testing it to see whether the communication is complete and the parsing process can start. The counter and the correctness are then reset, and we perform a test to see if the first six characters stored inside the buffer are equal to $GPRMC. Whenever we obtain a match, the correctness variable is incremented.

Keep in mind that this is a standard pattern and you will make use of it in other scenarios as well. If all of our data checks turn out to be true, the correctness variable is equal to six and this in turn means that our tests are correct. This process assures us that we are using the correct NMEA $GPRMC sequence and therefore we can parse the data. Once we divide the string by storing the position of every single comma separator, we perform the same process for the "*" symbol. We need to tell the difference between the characters and determine in which section of the message they belong. This is why we also use a number of switch / case statements. We need them to be able to print the correct messages that contain the GPS data we are looking for. Lastly, we finish the project with a "for" loop where we begin with the j index by using the array index at a certain position. Based on the position of each separator, we start progressively incrementing every single value. This allows us to basically parse and use location data as necessary with the help of our module. At this point, we can use this information for a variety of purposes and create a number of projects. For instance, we can combine the data with visualization techniques and create a program which records your location. We can store this data every 10 seconds on the EEPROM we discussed earlier and then use it to create a graphical representation of it.

During this section you may have been asking yourself what the point of this project is when we don't have the ability to move around with the Arduino in our pocket. This is a power related problem, as we obviously require enough energy to power both the Arduino as well as the GPS module, while also being able to walk on the street with it. This is where we start discussing the problem of autonomy. Let's see what we can do to make the board mobile and usable in a lot more scenarios.

Arduino Autonomy

To refresh your memory, the Arduino can be powered in two different ways. We either connect it to a computer via a USB cable, or we use an external power source, such as batteries. So far, we relied mostly on working with a USB power supply because it's the easiest and most practical way to build a project. However, in cases such as our GPS project example, mobility is essential and without it, the project becomes nearly useless. Now, keep in mind that the board rarely requires more than 50mA worth of power, however, in most cases you will have a certain number of external devices and circuits connected to it. We've already seen in an earlier example how quickly a set of LED lights can add up to that power requirement.

This doesn't mean that you should immediately give up on using a USB power supply, however. There are projects that simply cannot function without a connection to a computer via the USB cable. For instance, for data communication purposes this type of connection is mandatory and you can't go around it. With that being said, this is in fact the main reason we need a USB connection. Another issue we need to consider is the amount of power our project consumes, because the board can only handle up to 500mA through the USB port. If we go beyond that amount we risk serious damage to the hardware.

With that being said, if you're considering external power sources, there are two kinds you can opt for. You either go with batteries or a power adapter. We briefly used both methods in previous projects, but now is the time to expand on both of these power sources so that you can decide how your project can benefit the most.

Using Batteries

As you may recall, both the Arduino Uno as well as Arduino Mega can function by using an external power source ranging from 6 V to 20 V. However, the standard practice for optimal use is to use power supply with a range between 7 V and 12 V instead. 9 V is considered by many to be the ideal amount of voltage. Now, before we connect an external power supply to the Arduino, we need to handle the power jumper. This means that our first step is to place the jumper on the board's external power supply side which is labeled with EXT. This step is valid for a number of boards, however make sure to read up on your model because some of them are slightly different.

Now let's connect the power supply to the board with some simple wiring. All you need to do is grab a standard 9 V battery and connect its positive terminal to the Arduino's VIN pin and the negative terminal to the GND pin. Keep in mind that while the 9V battery is recommended due to the VIN pin's 12V limit, you can also opt for a 12V battery. If you choose to take this route, make sure that the battery doesn't supply you with a current value higher than 500 mA.

That's it! The power supply is connected, and now the battery will feed the Arduino and any external devices connected to it with enough power. But what if the 9V or 12V battery is too big and too heavy for your project? Not a problem. There are other types of batteries you can go with. For instance, we have the coin-sized cell batteries that can supply you with enough power while weighing as much as a feather. With this type of battery, however, you will need to purchase a cell battery holder in order to properly connect it to the board. Another limitation to keep in mind is the fact that a regular cell battery can supply you with 3.6 V and 110 mAh, and this might not be enough to power your project if you are working with an Arduino Uno, for instance. In this case, you may have to consider using an Arduino Pro Mini instead, as it requires only 3.3 V to operate.

When we're talking about power supply alternatives, you should also consider using the Arduino Pro Mini, as it doesn't require a large power source and it can also be embedded into other systems. The board is small and can easily be hidden inside walls, or plastic containers that fit inside your pocket. It is an excellent tool that provides you with all the mobility you could possibly need. If you choose to go with mini, however, you also have the option of using polymer lithium ion batteries, as they are perfect for autonomous devices.

Now, the question remains: what if we require a lot more power than batteries can provide us with? The answer is power adaptors!

Using Power Adaptors

Sometimes we have too many devices connected to the board for batteries to suffice. This is when we have to rely on an external power supply that isn't as limited and can also provide us with the mobility we need. Luckily, power adapters are readily available and an Arduino adapter is easy to come by. Just keep in mind that if you opt for an off the shelf adapter, you need to make sure that it is a DC adapter with an output voltage between 9 V and 12 V. You also need to guarantee a minimum of 250 mA current, or better yet 500 mA. Keep in mind that when it comes to power adapters you don't have to limit yourself to 500 mA, you can go even for 1 A. Finally, you need to make sure that the adapter comes with a center positive 2.1 mm power plug.

Once you make sure that your power adapter is with the center of the connector as the positive part, you need to start considering the voltage and current features. Examine the product information that comes with your adapter and check for labels such as OUTPUT: 12 VDC 1 A. You can also go with the 5 A version of that same adapter. Keep in mind that the current is supplied only by what you already have in your circuit. If you purchase a power adapter that releases a higher current, the circuit will not be damaged simply because it will only receive as much current as it needs. This is why there are a great number of adapters out there that can be used with the Arduino.

Always remember that when working with power adapters, you will have to calculate the current inside the circuit. This is where Ohm's law comes back into play, as we discussed it in an earlier chapter. You will have to consult the datasheet of a certain component in order to check how much current goes through it. Let's take an RGB LED for instance. The forward current may be around 20 mA with the possibility of hitting 30 mA at its peak use. This means that if we are connecting 5 such LEDs and enabling them to use the maximum amount of power to achieve the highest brightness, we will have to perform the following calculation: 5 * (20 + 20 + 20) = 300 mA. The three values come from the fact that RGB LEDs need to light up the red, blue, and green. This result would refer to the normal use of these LEDs, however the peak would be around 450 mA. At this point the lights are turned on at their maximum potential. Don't forget that a common strategy to reduce the power when working with LEDs is to turn them all in quick succession and not simultaneously. This reduces the amount of power they require and your project could benefit from more LEDs without the extra power.

We won't dig deeper into the mathematical calculations, but you should always consider the basic rules of electricity whenever you are attempting to perform an accurate calculation of your energy consumption. At this point you might want to consider using an Ampere meter or voltmeter. The voltmeter is used to measure the voltage that is running between point A and point B, while the Ampere meter measures the current between certain points across your circuit. However, even if you are using these tools, you should consider making the calculations as well and pay attention in order not to override the board's pin capacity, or the USB 450 mA limit.

CHAPTER 7: NETWORKING

In this chapter we are going to discuss creating networks with multiple Arduino boards and computers, and make them communicate with each other through various network protocols. Once you learn about creating data networks, we are going to progress to building Ethernet links between the devices. This step is crucial because it will provide you with the knowledge you need to build any project that relies on the Internet. We will also explore ways of developing Bluetooth communications, as well as methods of connecting the Arduino to other computers without using cumbersome network cables. Don't forget that many projects require mobility, and connecting your board to the Internet without any wires can open up a great deal of options.

But before we get started, you should ask yourself what a network really is when you strip it down to the basics. A network can be simply described as a system of various components connected to each other. This definition encompasses a variety of networks, including electrical grids, highways, as well as data networks. Naturally, in this section, we are interested in data networks that already surround us in our daily life. We have video service networks, phone networks, global communication networks, and so on.

Open Systems Interconnection

We will focus on different kinds of networks and discuss how we can share data from different types of media. However, before we start discussing the relation between Arduino boards and network implementations, we are going to explore the Open Systems Interconnection model which was developed in the 70s. Why are going to talk about something so old? Because this model's purpose is to define the requirements around various communication systems. It is a layer focused model that basically defines which features and protocols are needed in order to develop a communication system.

When we're discussing communication protocols, we are referring to a system of rules and formats that provide the base for communication between a minimum of two parties. With every single layer we have one or multiple functionality implementations and every single entity interacts with the layer below it and provides the resources needed by the layer above it. Essentially, protocols enable objects from one host to interact with the equivalent objects from another host, but inside the same layer. One host transmits data to another host, in this case known as a payload sometimes, which is then passed to the layer below. In order to retrieve this data, a header and footer are required to be added to it, depending on which protocol is used. This process is referred to as encapsulation and it goes all the way down to the bottom layer, which is the physical one. The receiver requires the flow of bits to be modulated, and the data needs to pass through the layers and communicate the flow to each one of them by using the aforementioned headers and footers. These elements are then deleted all along the layer path. This is known as decapsulation. When the data's journey is complete and the receiver receives it, it can finally process it. Keep in mind that at every level, the two hosts are communicating to each other by using the protocol data unit, or PDU for short. As a follow up, the service data unit (SDU) is also called. This type of data is passed down from one layer to another, only downwards and only to layers that haven't been encapsulated yet. Every single layer examines the received data as an element which either adds or deletes headers and footers by following the rules set by the protocol.

With that being said, let's take a look at all the layers and protocols in order to gain a better understanding.

Layers and Protocols

As mentioned earlier, in this section we are going to briefly discuss the purpose of every single layer and explore certain examples of protocols.

1. **The Physical Layer**: This is the layer that determines which physical specifications are needed in order to establish data communication. This includes pin structure, voltage, impedance, network adapters, host bus adapters and so on. The first major function this layer performs is the initialization of a connection to a communication channel. This also includes the termination of

said connection. Participation in the control processes that involve shared data is another function provided by the physical layer, together with the ability to process the conversion between communicated data and the signals which transport it. Here are some of the most popular standards that are found in this layer: Bluetooth, USB, and optic fiber networks.

2. **Data Link Layer**: This layer is in fact divided into two sections. One is the media access control, and the other is the logical link control. Both of them provide the ability to transfer the data between various network systems, as well as an error detection service. This last function looks for errors inside the previous layer and can even fix them. Here are some of the most popular standards that belong to this layer: Ethernet, Wi-Fi, and I2C.

3. **The Network Layer**: This layer allows us to transfer data in-between hosts that are located in separate networks. It provides us with routing, fragmentation, and reassembly and error reports. The routing is needed in order to give the hosts the ability to communicate with each other. Fragmentation and reassembly go hand in hand, as these functions cut or divide the data into smaller pieces for easier transmission and then reassemble them at the final destination. The router is the main component here because it needs to be connected to multiple networks in order to allow the data to travel

between them.

4. **The Transport Layer**: This layer ensures the data transmission between the users, and it is located in between the network layer and the application layer. It provides us with error control, flow control, and the segmentation or desegmentation of data. The protocols related to this layer are either connection-based, or state-based, which means that we can monitor travelling data segments and in case they fail to arrive at the destination (failed transmission), we can restart the transmission process automatically. There are two standards that you should be aware of when discussing this layer, namely TCP and UDP. As you may already know, TCP is the one that is connection-focused because it maintains the communication by making sure all transmission components are working as intended. UDP, on the other hand, is stateless and its purpose is to resend a transmission request when something goes wrong.

5. **The Application Layers**: These layers are the final step of a network transmission and therefore they are part of the OSI model. Here are some examples of client / server applications: FTP for basic file transfers, POP3 and other applications for mail services, SSH for secure shell communication, and finally HTTP for web browsing and more.

IP Addresses and Ports

Before we can start wiring the Arduino to a local area network, we need to cover some basic aspects regarding IPs and ports. Don't worry, this won't turn into a full blown course about networks and network administration. We will only stick to the bare bone requirements.

With that being said, ask yourself what exactly is an IP address? The simplest way of defining it would be as a numerical address which is referenced by any device that seeks to communicate over a certain network. Keep in mind that there are two types of IP addresses, namely IPv4 and IPv6. This is worth taking note of, because for the time being only IPv4 is relevant to us because it is the only version that is available to users. Currently IPv6 is not supported by a great number of routers and servers, therefore making such a connection could cause complications. IPv4 represents the addresses that are coded over 32 bits, while IPv6 represents the addresses with a length of 128 bits. As you already know, an IP address is written as a collection of 4 bytes that are separated by a point, thus making it easily readable. While a regular address looks something like 192.122.1.555, some of them have a more unique structure and cannot be routed through the internet.

The next question is, what is a subnet? This is a method of splitting a network into smaller fractions. As you probably noticed, a standard network configuration contains the IP address, a subnet mask, and a gateway. The IP together with the subnet mask are the elements that determine the range of the network.

This is essential to obtaining information on whether a transmitter can directly communicate through the receiver via a network connection. Keep in mind that if the receiver is found inside the same network, communication is direct, however if it is on the outside (in a different network), that transmitter needs to use the gateway as an intermediary which routes the data until it reaches its destination. The gateway contains all the information it needs regarding which network it connects to. This means that it can send data to various networks, and even filter some of it if we implement some kind of rule set with specific limitations. With that being said, the subnet has a similar structure to the IP address. Here's an example of a subnet mask: 255.254.255.0.

Lastly, we have the communication port which is connected to the transport layer we discussed earlier. Let's assume we want to transmit a message to a host for a certain application. The receiver can only receive this message by being in listening mode, which means that we need an open communication port. Normally, an application is capable of opening its own port, however you should keep in mind that once it's open and used, a different application can no longer have access to it. The end result is a highly versatile and interconnected data trading system.

Another aspect to consider is that if we need to transmit data to a certain host, but for multiple applications, we need to specify that the message is meant for said host, to different ports corresponding to each application. As you might assume, this doesn't mean that we can proceed however we want. There are various standards designed for global communications and we need to adhere to the set rules. For instance, the HTTP protocol that is related to web-based data exchanges requires TCP port 80. On the other hand, we have UDP port 53 that is required for any operation involving DNS.

With that being said, you should now have enough basic knowledge to start working on your first Arduino networking project. Let's start learning how to wire the board to a wired Ethernet system.

Using Wired Ethernet

As you probably know, Ethernet refers to the local area network you are already using on a daily basis. Normally, Arduino boards do not offer you the ability to use the Ethernet, and therefore you need to use an Arduino Ethernet Shield and a 100BASE-T cable. For this project we are going to work with Arduino UNO R3. If you are planning to use a different model, please make sure to always check the device's datasheet because certain things are bound to differ from our example. With that being said, the reason we need to use these two components is the fact that they provide us with the necessary network connectivity and the aforementioned cable is much longer than your default USB cable.

The Arduino Ethernet Shield is in fact an Ethernet module that is usually sold together with a PoE device. In case you don't know, PoE stands for Power over Ethernet, and it basically is a power supply that feeds other modules through an Ethernet connection. In our example, however, we aren't going to be using the PoE.

Now let's start developing a system that uses Ethernet communication between our board and a small program. The plan is to connect the Arduino to the computer through the Ethernet. We are going to be sending a message from the board to the computer program through the UDP. Our program will react by sending messages in return, which as a result will flip an LED switch on to let us know that communication is established. For this step we are going to connect a simple switch that toggles the Arduino's default LED light. Remember that the connection to the computer is established through the Ethernet cable.

In order to provide our board with the ability to transmit messages through the Ethernet cable, and therefore the network, we need to define the specific conventions that are required by the firmware. For our programming, we will have to use the Ethernet Library because it enables us to use specifically network related functions and features. Keep in mind that this library, like the others mentioned throughout the book, is available straight from the core. Now let's take a look at the code and discuss the process in more detail afterwards:

```
#include <SPI.h>

#include <Ethernet.h>

#include <EthernetUdp.h>
```

```
#include <SPI.h>

#include <Ethernet.h>

#include <EthernetUdp.h>

// Defining the switch and the LED

const int switchPin = 2; // switch pin

const int ledPin = 13; // LED pin

int switchState = 0; // variable needed to store the current
state of the switch

int lastSwitchState = LOW;

long lastDebounceTime = 0;

long debounceDelay = 50;

// Defining the network

// defining the IP address, port and a MAC address for the
board

byte mac[] = {

0xDE, 0xAD, 0xBE, 0xEF, 0xFE, 0xED };

IPAddress ipArduino(192, 168, 1, 123);

unsigned int ArduinoPort = 9999;

// The computer's UDP port and IP address
```

// We need to modify the port and the IP based on our configuration

```
IPAddress ipComputer(192, 168, 1, 222);

unsigned int ComputerPort = 10000;
```

// Send/receive buffer

```
char      packetBuffer[UDP_TX_PACKET_MAX_SIZE]; //buffer
```

// Need to instantiate the Ethernet UDP instance to send and receive packets through the UDP

```
EthernetUDP Udp;

void setup() {

    pinMode(ledPin, OUTPUT); // set the LED pin as an output

    pinMode(switchPin, INPUT); // set the switch pin as an input

    // starting Ethernet and UDP

    Ethernet.begin(mac,ipArduino);

    Udp.begin(ArduinoPort);

}
```

```
void loop(){

// if a packed is received, read it into the packet buffer

    if                              (Udp.parsePacket())
    Udp.read(packetBuffer,UDP_TX_PACKET_MAX_SI
    ZE);

    if (packetBuffer == "Light") digitalWrite(ledPin,
    HIGH);

    else if (packetBuffer == "Dark") digitalWrite(ledPin,
    LOW);

// read the state of the digital pin

    int readInput = digitalRead(switchPin);

    if (readInput != lastSwitchState)

    {

        lastDebounceTime = millis();

    }

    if ( (millis() - lastDebounceTime) > debounceDelay )

    {

        switchState = readInput;

    }
```

```
lastSwitchState = readInput;

if (switchState == HIGH)

{

// send a packet to processing if the switch is pressed

Udp.beginPacket(ipComputer, ComputerPort);

Udp.write('Pushed');

Udp.endPacket();

}

else

{
// send a packet to processing if the switch is pressed

Udp.beginPacket(ipComputer, ComputerPort);

Udp.write('Released');

Udp.endPacket();

}

delay(10);

}
```

As always, we start by importing the required library, in this case being the Ethernet library. The next step is to declare all of the variables that are needed to handle the LED, switch debouncing, and network features. Once we've made the preparations, we need to start defining the shield's MAC address, which is unique to every device and can be found in the accompanying user manual or on a sticker glued to the back of the module. Keep in mind that this means you have to check your own address and type it inside the code, otherwise our little project won't work.

Once that is taken care of, we include the Arduino's IP address. In this case we need to make sure that the address can be reached. The way to make sure your computer can reach the IP is by working on one single network, or on a different network but with a router as the intermediary between the two networks. Just make sure that your IP address is unique to the local network. The next step is to choose the UPD port. This is needed to establish proper communications, and in our example we are working with network parameters that are connected to the personal computer. Then we define a buffer where we deposit the current received messages. Pay attention to the UDP_TX_PACKET_MAX_SIZE constant that we declared, as it is used to save some memory. If you check the library's documentation you will see that it is included with it. Next up, we need to instantiate our EthernetUDP object so that we can transmit and receive data through UDP.

The next section of our code is as usual the setup function, where we declare the statements for the LED, the switch, and the Ethernet. At the start of the block, we establish the Ethernet connection by using our IP and MAC addresses. Next, the UDP port is opened and defined. Then, we have the loop section, which as you can see is a little bit more complex than in our previous projects. We start by performing a verification that checks to confirm whether Arduino is receiving any packets. If a packet was registered, the parse packet function is called if the size is not zero. Keep in mind that this function is also part of the Ethernet library. Once the result is established, the data is read and then stored inside the packet buffer. The final step of this stage is to check whether the variable is equal to light or dark, which refers to the Arduino switching the LED on or off. We also perform a check to see if the switch is pressed or not, and based on the result a UDP message is transmitted.

Keep in mind that this is only the first half of our project. We still need to develop the program required to communicate as planned over the Ethernet. Let's start first with the code for this application and then discuss it in detail:

```
import hypermedia.net.*;

UDP udp; // defining our UDP object

String currentMessage;

String ip = "192.168.1.123"; // the IP address belonging to
the Arduino
```

```
int port = 9999; // the UDP port belonging to the Arduino


void setup() {

    size(700, 700);

    noStroke();

    fill(0);

    udp = new UDP( this, 10000 ); // need to create a UDP
    socket

    udp.listen( true ); // check for message

}

void draw()

    {

        ellipse(width/2, height/2, 230, 230);

    }

void receive( byte[] data ) {

    if ( data.length == 6 || data.length == 8 )

    {

        for (int i=0; i < data.length; i++)
```

```
        {
            currentMessage += data[i];

        }
    // if the message is equal to Pushed
    // then answer with "Light"
        if (currentMessage == "Pushed")

        {
            udp.send("Light", ip, port );

            fill(255);

        }

        else if (currentMessage == "Released")

            {
                udp.send("Dark", ip, port );

                fill(0);

            }

        }

    }
```

Once we import the hypermedia library, we define the UDP object and a string type variable which holds the current received message. Keep in mind that we have to define the IP address of the Arduino here as well, just like we did in the first half of the project. We also need to define the open port which is available to the Arduino. In both blocks of code the port is 9999. As you may have guessed, all of this information needs to precisely match what we defined earlier in the board's firmware. Next, we have a setup function where we define several parameters followed by the instantiation of the UDP socket to port 10000. This UDP port is then set to listening mode because we need to wait for any incoming communication.

Next, we have the draw function where we simply define a circle. Then the receive function is used as a callback for the incoming packets. The size of the packets is measured and verified in bytes because we need only two messages. We are looking to reach a push or release, and therefore we test whether the packet length is either six or eight bytes. Every other packet that doesn't fit our definition will go ignored and unprocessed. Keep in mind that our testing system isn't perfect and there is room for improvement. We are using only a basic check and for the purpose of this exercise, it works well enough. If you want to stretch your wings, feel free to seek for ways to improve it.

The Arduino reacts accordingly whether it receives a "pushed" or "released" message. If "light" is communicated, the circle will be filled with a white color, and if "dark" is communicated, the circle will be filled with a black color. That's it! We now have a simple communication protocol that relies on the Ethernet and UDP. Now, let's broaden our networking horizon and discuss Bluetooth communications.

Using Bluetooth

Another functionality you have access to with the Arduino is Bluetooth. As you may know, this is a type of wireless tech that allows you transfer data over very short distances. The data exchange is performed using a short wavelength radio transmission. This system also permits you to create personal area networks which can be implemented on computers, phones, and other devices. Keep in mind that not all Arduino models have Bluetooth technology readily available. If you are using a common board like the Arduino Uno, you will have to purchase an external Bluetooth module.

At this point you might be feeling somewhat frustrated due to having to deal with so many external modules because the board doesn't offer them natively. You really shouldn't. From a project design perspective, it's considered better to use a basic board to which you connect only what you actually need. For instance, there's no point in working with a big board that already comes with an external power supply, a Wi-Fi module, and a Bluetooth module when all you need to achieve is lighting up one single LED. Always go with a generic board for the core of your project and add only what tools you need.

With that being said, we are going to work with the Arduino Uno, which requires a Bluetooth module to be connected to it. We are going to work on a project that requires the use of Processing. This project will involve a Processing environment where if a mouse click is detected, the application will transmit a message using the Bluetooth connection, to the board, which in turn will light up its LED to notify us that the message is received. We are going to be using the RN41 Bluetooth device in this example, so make sure you check your device's datasheet to make the appropriate connections and modifications. You will also need a computer with Bluetooth capabilities. Keep in mind that many desktops don't come with this feature, so you may have to purchase a separate Bluetooth module for your PC, or use a laptop instead. All laptops come with Bluetooth, generally. Now, let's take a look at the firmware:

```
// handling our LED

const int ledPin = 13; // the Arduino's pin connected to the LED

void setup() {

    pinMode(ledPin, OUTPUT); // we need to set the LED pin as the output

    Serial.begin(9600); // starting serial communication

}
```

```
void loop()

{

if (Serial.available() > 0) {

    incomingByte = Serial.read();

    if (incomingByte == 1) digitalWrite(ledPin,
    HIGH);

    else if (incomingByte == 0) digitalWrite(ledPin,
    LOW);

}

}
```

All we had to do here is instantiate the serial communication with our Bluetooth device. We also have to perform a verification process to see whether there are any bytes coming from it and then parse them. The LED is then switched on if a message is available, or switched off if there isn't. Now let's take a look at the code for our application:

```
import processing.serial.*;

Serial port;

int bgcolor, fgcolor;

void setup() {

    size(700, 700);
```

```
    background(0);

    stroke(255);

    bgcolor = 0;

    fgcolor = 255;

    println(Serial.list());

    port = new Serial(this, Serial.list()[2], 9600);

}

void draw() {

    background(bgcolor);

    stroke(fgcolor);

    fill(fgcolor);

    rect(100, 100, 500, 500);

}

void mousePressed() {

    if (mouseX > 100 && mouseX < 600 && mouseY >
    100 && mouseY < 600)

    {

        bgcolor = 255;
```

```
        fgcolor = 0;

        port.write('1');

    }

}

void mouseReleased() {

    bgcolor = 0;

    fgcolor = 255;

    port.write('0');

}
```

Now that we have the code, let's take a closer look and understand what's happening. Processing's serial number needs to be imported, as discussed in previous projects. As usual, we have the setup block of the code where we define the drawing elements and print the list of the serial device to Processing. Next, we have the draw function where we prepare our environment. We set up the background color, the stroke color, and the fill color based on self-explanatory variables. We basically draw a square and then we introduce the mouse pressed and mouse released functions to be called whenever a mouse event is registered. When the mouse button is pressed, our application verifies the position of the mouse cursor during this action. As you can see in the code, we have designated a specific area inside our environment, which is the square, and if we press the button within its confines we receive visual information. This lets us know that the information was transmitted and received, and the digital write function writes the value of 1 to the module. In a similar fashion, when we release the button, the function writes the 0 value, to let the Bluetooth module know that the mouse button was released. All of this information is transmitted to the Arduino board, which as a result will switch the LED light on or off.

That's it! We have successfully implemented an external Bluetooth module that gives us the ability to communicate over short distances. One thing worth noting at this point is that the library we used isn't generally necessary. The Bluetooth module is capable of sending and receiving data on its own without any kind of assistance. We only implement this library when we want to send serial data. However, in our example we're working with serial data between the Arduino and the module, and that is why we're using the library.

Now that we've covered the Ethernet direct connection and Bluetooth as well, let's discuss data communication over a Wi-Fi connection.

Using Wi-Fi

Now that you know more about network communications and we worked with short range Wi-Fi, we can finally explore wireless medium range communication that you will frequently use when building your own projects.

But what exactly is Wi-Fi? We can summarize this technology as a set of wireless protocols controlled by the IEEE 802.11 standards which describe the features and rules of wireless local area networks. Basically, several hosts with Wi-Fi connections, or modules, can transmit and receive information by relying on their IP stacks. Keep in mind that there are several networking modes that this type of communication uses and in each one of them hosts connect and communicate differently.

For instance, we have infrastructure mode, where the hosts use an access point for communication with each other. The hosts, as well as the access point, have to be defined using the identical service set identifier. This identifier is basically a network name that allows the hosts to use it as a reference point. One of the characteristics of this mode that sets it apart from others is that every single host has to go through the access point before gaining access to the global network. This means that security is much tighter than in other modes. There are other modes as well, such as the ad hoc mode, where the connection between hosts is direct, or bridge mode where several access points are linked to each other. However, we won't dig into these any deeper.

The main component we need to focus on is the Arduino Wi-Fi shield. This is what gives our board the ability to perform a wireless connection. It's also worth noting that this device also comes with a slot where you can insert an SD card, meaning you have increased storage capabilities as well. The shield provides you with wireless connection features, network encryption methods, serial debugging features for the module, as well as a mini USB connector so that you can update the shield's firmware.

Connecting the Wi-Fi module is a simple task, as there's no wiring involved. You simply plug in it and you feed it some code. Now we are going to connect the shield and test a simple connection using the ConnectNoEncryption example that can be found inside the WiFi library. Using the native library, we will have access to everything we need to perform a wireless connection to any network. Now let's take a look at the code and discuss the entire process:

```
#include <WiFi.h>

char ssid[] = "yourNetwork"; // introduce your network's name

int status = WL_IDLE_STATUS; // wifi status

void setup() {

//wait for this port to open once you initialize the serial

    Serial.begin(9600);

// performing a check for the presence of the module

    if (WiFi.status() == WL_NO_SHIELD) {

        Serial.println("WiFi shield not present");
// don't continue
```

```
    while(true)

    delay(30) ;
}
// try to connect to the Wifi network
    while ( status != WL_CONNECTED) {

    Serial.print("Attempting to connect to open SSID: ");

    Serial.println(ssid);

    status = WiFi.begin(ssid);

// adding a 10 second delay to wait for the connection
    delay(10000);

}

// print out data once the connection is established
    Serial.print("You're connected to the network");

    printCurrentNet();

    printWifiData();

}
```

```
void loop() {

// perform a connection check in 10 second intervals

   delay(10000);

   printCurrentNet();

}

void printWifiData() {

// print the module's IP address

   IPAddress ip = WiFi.localIP();

   Serial.print("IP Address: ");

   Serial.println(ip);

   Serial.println(ip);

// printing MAC address:

   byte mac[6];

   WiFi.macAddress(mac);

   Serial.print("MAC address: ");

   Serial.print(mac[5],HEX);

   Serial.print(":");

   Serial.print(mac[4],HEX);
```

```
    Serial.print(":");

    Serial.print(mac[3],HEX);

    Serial.print(":");

    Serial.print(mac[2],HEX);

    Serial.print(":");

    Serial.print(mac[1],HEX);

    Serial.print(":");

    Serial.println(mac[0],HEX);
// printing subnet mask:

    IPAddress subnet = WiFi.subnetMask();

    Serial.print("NetMask: ");

    Serial.println(subnet);
// printing gateway address:

    IPAddress gateway = WiFi.gatewayIP();

    Serial.print("Gateway: ");

    Serial.println(gateway);
}
void printCurrentNet() {
```

```
// printing the SSID of the network you're connected to

    Serial.print("SSID: ");

    Serial.println(WiFi.SSID());

// printing the MAC address of the router you're connected to

    byte bssid[6];

    WiFi.BSSID(bssid);

    Serial.print("BSSID: ");

    Serial.print(bssid[5],HEX);

    Serial.print(":");

    Serial.print(bssid[4],HEX);

    Serial.print(":");

    Serial.print(bssid[3],HEX);

    Serial.print(":");

    Serial.print(bssid[2],HEX);

    Serial.print(":");

    Serial.print(bssid[1],HEX);

    Serial.print(":");
```

```
        Serial.println(bssid[0],HEX);

    // printing signal strength

        long rssi = WiFi.RSSI();

        Serial.print("signal strength (RSSI):");

        Serial.println(rssi);

    // printing type of encryption

        byte encryption = WiFi.encryptionType();

        Serial.print("Encryption Type:");

        Serial.println(encryption,HEX);

    }
```

Once we import the WiFi library, we have to name our network. Make sure to change this name to your own, otherwise the program won't work. With that in mind, let's move on to our setup section. We need to instantiate a serial connection and perform a verification procedure to make sure that the module is connected. This is why we use the Wi-Fi status function. If it returns the WL_NO_SHIELD constant, it simply means that there's no module present, and an infinite loop will be executed to recheck periodically. The same function can also return different values, and we state that if anything other than WL_CONNECTED is received, we print an argument which informs the connection attempt. At this point the WiFi.begin function will perform connection attempts for as long as there is no connection detected. We also included a 10 second delay so that the connection attempt is performed in intervals instead of bombarding the system too aggressively. Once the connection is successful, we print a serial message which specifies the connection status as "connected." The last piece of the puzzle involves two functions that print all the components that are connected to the status of the network and its parameters. In order to learn more about these elements, you should consult the reference guide that comes with the WiFi library. Once the network connection is established, data can be exchanged between the device, however don't forget that in this example we aren't using any kind of encryption methods. Using Wi-Fi without any type of security system can be dangerous and risky, because anyone could have access to the network and extract your data packets.

Now that you have all the knowledge you need regarding networks and communications, you should consider implementing an encryption system as your homework. You can use the WiFi library to add these security functions, so make sure to give the library's reference a good read as it contains everything you need to know.

CONCLUSION

You have finished absorbing everything *Arduino Programming: The Ultimate Intermediate Guide to Learn Arduino Programming Step By Step* has to offer! Congratulations! Now you have everything you need to go out on your own and start building the projects of your dreams. You learned how to connect any kind of module in order to extend the functionality of the Arduino board, and now you can finally start building more complex projects, such as robots! Start taking over the world and share everything with other Arduino fans and extend your knowledge about electronics, computers, and programming.

Remember, if you feel intimidated by certain topics, or if you think you aren't that great at coding, you shouldn't give up! There's a solution for everything and there are many online communities out there willing to help. Explore the applications step by step, read more module datasheets and reference guides, examine project schematics, and start building! The things you can achieve with the Arduino are incredible, and you should continue practicing because nobody becomes an engineer or a developer overnight without practice.

Congratulations on continuing with the Arduino guide series and advancing to the next level! Keep this guide close, and continue expanding your knowledge with more books, more tutorials, and more practice. Start building your army of Arduino robots today and conquer the world, because why not?